TALES OF
OLD GLAMORGAN

Tales of Old Glamorgan

Wendy Hughes

ISBN: 0-86381-287-2

Cover and illustrations: Trefor Davies

*First published in 1994 by Gwasg Carreg Gwalch,
Iard yr Orsaf, Llanrwst, Gwynedd, Wales.*

☎ 0492 642031

Printed and published in Wales

DEDICATION

For my mother, Ethel Mary Davies, in this her 90th year. Despite being totally blind for over 40 years she is a survivor, a conqueror of adversity and a true fighting spirit of Wales.

Contents

Introduction

Every inch of Wales, the land of the fiery red dragon, Merlin the Wizard and King Arthur, is steeped in its own special brand of tales. It is the land of poetry and song, castles and princes, Celtic druids and warriors, of heroes and heroines, which paint a vivid picture of hazy days of adventure, charm and mystery.

The art of story telling goes back a long time. No doubt it all began when our neolithic ancestors sat at their cave entrances watching the flickering embers of the fire, and telling yarns to enthral and excite. The tales of King Arthur and his Knights are famous. Whilst every child born in Wales can recall the romantic stories of *Y Mabinogi,* those tales which rank with Chaucer's tales for importance in European literature.

But each county has its own treasure trove of stories too, and the county of Glamorgan is no exception. For between those rolling hills reverberate the tales of intrigue, bringing alive a special imprint that is the pulsating heart of the county.

The name Glamorgan is derived from *Gwlad Morgan* — the land of Morgan, after Morgan ap Athrwys, a native prince. He was first mentioned in the Book of Llandaf or *Liber Landavensis* — a book that contains a collection of copies of charters and other documents dating from the 5th century to about 1132. Once it was one of the largest counties in Wales, but local government reorganisation in 1974 divided it into three — Mid, South and West Glamorgan. For the purpose of this book I have returned to the boundary lines of Old Glamorgan, an area which extends from the deeply scarred industrial valleys to the rural aspects of the Vale of Glamorgan emerging into the spectacular scenery of the Gower Peninsula.

The arms of Glamorgan, three red chevrons on a shield of gold, are the blazon of the famous de Clare family who were the lords of Glamorgan from 1218-1314. The chevron first appeared on a seal of Gilbert de Clare between the years 1138-1148, and is the earliest known example of an insignia exhibited on a seal.

In this book I recall forty-five of the incredible tales that brought the county alive — to include them all would be impossible as the book would run into several volumes. The selection includes my favourite legends, fables of fairies and magic, foxes and snakes, myths to enchant, as well as stories of devils, witches and ghosts. Also included are a mixture of true events and people which have given the county of Glamorgan its uniqueness. Some are quite short but worth retelling. For others there are perhaps several versions, so where possible I have tried to recount the most authentic. Sometimes, through the passage of time, this has proved impossible, so I hope I will be forgiven for taking the liberty of choosing my own favourite version.

In a generation where video, television and computer games are so prominent, story telling is fast becoming a dying art. I hope that, in some small way, this book will help to keep the culture alive, and encapsulate the romance of Glamorgan.

So sit back, enjoy the choice of stories, and perhaps you will even feel inspired to visit the many places which still exist. Let your imagination flow, meander down the valleys and sit and dream of the characters and adventures of an age that is entwined in mystery and intrigue.

The Conquest of Glamorgan

Our first story, how the Normans won the kingdom of Glamorgan, is a truly romantic one, steeped in legend, yet one that has lost none of its magic through re-telling. No doubt, through the passage of time, much has been added to the original so that today it is impossible for historians to distinguish fact from fiction.

The story opens in the 11th century with Iestyn ap Gwrgan, the Lord of Glamorgan. In those days Glamorgan was a kingdom of itself, and even now is considered to be the most important county in Wales, in which Cardiff, the capital of Wales is situated.

Iestyn was constantly at war with his disagreeable neighbour Rhys ap Tewdwr, the Prince of South Wales. Some say these wars continued because Iestyn refused to acknowledge Rhys' claim to be overlord of the land. Others claim they were caused because of Rhys' enormous love for Iestyn's wife, a woman of outstanding beauty.

Finding himself unable to cope with the many battles that ensued Iestyn sent for Einion ap Collwyn, a brother of a former prince of Deheubarth, and asked him to seek military help from the Normans. Iestyn was so eager to obtain help he promised Einion that if successful he would be rewarded with the hand of his daughter, Nest, and a marriage dowry of the lordship of Miskin.

Einion had many friends among the Normans so it was easy for him to enlist the help of Baron Robert Fitzhamon subject to certain conditions, including a promise to the Baron that he would receive a 'mile of gold' for his services. Once the agreement was made Robert Fitzhamon, with twelve knights and 3,000 men-at-arms, set sail and landed at Porthkerry in 1090 or 1091. It is believed they crossed the ford on the Severn near the Caston or Black Rock.

The combined Welsh and Norman armies attacked and defeated Rhys ap Tewdwr and his army at Bryn-y-beddau near Hirwaun, just within the borders of the county. History does not record if Fitzhamon's conquest was an easy or a hard one. We do know, however, that Rhys fled with his life, but was pursued and killed on the brow of a hill in Glyn Rhondda, later to be renamed Penrhys in commemoration of this sad event.

With the task successfully accomplished the Normans received their payment at a place called Pentre Meyrick, near Bridgend. Legend states that the gold coins were laid side by side along the road for a mile, which became known as *Milltir Aur* — the Golden Mile. Having received their promised reward the Normans bade Einion farewell and departed.

Iestyn, having nothing to fear since his powerful enemy was now dead, refused to fulfil his promise to Einion and allow him a daughter in marriage. Enraged at being cheated, Einion jumped on his horse and galloped after Fitzhamon and his men.

With the two Welshmen locked in conflict the Norman Baron saw this as an ideal chance to gain the county for himself and returned immediately. The Normans met Iestyn and his men at Mynydd Bychan — The Great Heath, now Cardiff's Heath Park. In the battle that followed the Welsh lord of Glamorgan was slain.

Fitzhamon took possession of Glamorgan and Einion not only won his bride, but was rewarded with the Lordship of Senghenydd. But in true Welsh tradition Einion became known as *Einion Fradwr*, Einion the traitor, and from that day onwards he was never accepted by the Welsh people again.

Fitzhamon divided Iestyn's territory between himself, twelve of his chief barons and a handful of Welshman. One of these barons was a man called Payn de Turberville — 'The Demon' — and there is an interesting tale about how he received Coity as part of the winner's booty.

It is said that de Turberville asked Fitzhamon which principality he could claim as a reward for his services. Fitzhamon repied, 'Here are arms, here are men, go, get it where you can'. Turberville, who fancied Coity for himself immediately marched to Coity castle, demanding its chief, Lord Morgan, now a very old man, to surrender. Morgan appeared holding the hand of his daughter Sibyll in one hand and his sword in the other. Morgan offered him the castle if he would marry his daughter, the heiress. If not he would have to win the castle by his sword. In true romantic form Morgan added, 'let not the blood of any of our men be spilt, but let this sword and arms of mine, and those of yours, decide who shall call the castle his own'.

Turberville did not reply but drew his sword from its scabbard, and smiled at the heiress. With one hand he presented his sword to the Welshman whilst with the other he embraced the girl claiming her as his bride. Soon Norman Knight and Welsh heiress became man and wife, the ancestors to a powerful Welsh family.

When Fitzhamon asked Turberville to pay tax he refused claiming he won his lands by marriage and not war. He, like the Welsh soldiers, considered the taxes to be the dues of Iestyn's successor, Caradog ap Iestyn, whom they acknowledged as the true Lord of Glamorgan. Fierce disputes between the two Normans followed until finally Turberville, together with his wife's brothers, succeeded in winning the argument. It was then agreed that Fitzhamon and Caradog ap Iestyn should jointly hold the feudal Lordship.

In those days the fox was regarded as the devil's informant and there are many stories told throughout Wales about the animal. For one such tale we must return to Einion Fradwr as it concerns his fate.

Several hundred years after the conquest in 1091, we are told a drover, whilst driving his cattle through the Vale of Glamorgan to the meat market in London, became tired. It had been a hot day and a long exhausting journey, so he decided to rest against a tree until he had gathered his strength to continue.

He had just settled himself down when he saw a fox with a haggard appearance and worried look upon its face creeping towards him. To the drover's amazement the fox sat besides him and spoke explaining that it was burdened with sorrow and distress and could not settle. On thinking he was hearing things the drover laughed, but when the fox became angry he recalled the old Welsh legends about the fox being the devil's messenger. He listened intently as the fox explained he was Einion ap Collwyn who had betrayed the Welsh to the Normans many years ago. As a punishment for his deeds, he was doomed to spend the rest of his eternity as a fox. As for the drover, we are told that from then onwards he avoided that particular route.

The Sinister Secrets of Cap Coch

During the late eighteenth century an old hostelry, called The New Inn, was a favourite haunt of smugglers and outlaws but, behind its door, hid a sinister secret. The inn was situated in a little hollow along a track that led from the main Bridgend to Merthyr Mawr road, the by-pass of today. This main road came to an abrupt end at the Ogmore River.

Stage coach passengers travelling from West Wales had to alight, walk across the ford and catch another coach to Ewenny where they could pick up the connection to London. Because of this stop many travellers preferred to go direct to Ewenny on foot or by horseback.

At this time Bridgend was the centre of the South Wales woollen and stocking industry and played host to many packmen, so called because they carried valuable goods such as flannel, wool skeins and stockings on meshed frames strapped to their broad shoulders. With the New Inn so ideally located it was a natural stopping place for those who wished to refresh themselves with a good night's rest before completing their journey. Sadly for many it was also their last.

The licensee, *Cap Coch* or Red Cap, had a mass of red hair and a beard, and an evil glint in his eyes. He was a very powerful man who, with his gang of outlaws and smugglers, terrorised the area. He had been to France and was sympathetic to the French Revolutionary movement and insisted on wearing the 'liberty' scarlet stockinet cap of the so called freedom fighter — hence the nickname. Cap Coch and his men organised frequent raids along the main road to attack the odd lone traveller but the richest pickings were to be had within the inn.

The travellers, who carried their merchandise in a pack covered with waterproof sheeting, were used also as message carriers and news vendors. By nature they were a talkative bunch easily tempted into the inn to share their news, many never to be seen again.

When bodies were dragged from the River Ogmore at an alarming rate, suspicion fell on the inn because they coincided always with the disappearance of travellers who had stayed there. Sadly for them there were no police and, whilst Cap Coch and his associates grew richer, the townspeople turned a 'blind eye' because there was always a ready market amongst them for the murdered mans goods.

Local people still retell the story of one packman who escaped with his life. One cold wet November evening he lost his way and, just as he reached the Merthyr Mawr road, he met a gypsy woman who begged some money from him. When he asked her where he could find a bed for the night, she replied that he would have to go some distance before he would find a safe house. She specifically warned him that the next house he would come to would be most unsafe and on no account was he to enter.

The traveller thanked her and set off on his way. Shortly he reached the glowing lights of the New Inn and could hear the babble of voices within. He was cold, wet and weary, and soon forgot the old woman's warnings. He pushed open the door and was warmly greeted by a man in a red cap. When he enquired about a bed for the night the man looked delighted and led him towards a table. A steaming bowl of soup, laced with sleep inducing herbs, was placed before him and he ate ravenously. Slowly the latch of the Inn door lifted and the old woman walked in, acknowledged the traveller by rubbing his shoulder as she passed before walking back out again.

As soon as the man had finished his meal he felt drowsy. He was led by two of Cap Coch's men to a ladder at the top of which was an open trap door leading to the loft. Inside he found a heap of straw and, being too tired to worry about a comfortable bed, threw down his bulging wallet for a pillow. He eased himself onto the straw and sank into a deep sleep.

Suddenly he was woken by a thunderous knock at the door of the

Inn and, through a crack in the floorboards, saw a group of rough looking men enter the room below. All were carrying heavy loads and excitedly recounting their adventures. Immediately he recalled the old woman's words but before he could do anything about it he fell back into a deep sleep.

The following morning Cap Coch called him and when he entered the kitchen he saw no signs of the goods he had seen the previous night. After a hearty breakfast he bid his host farewell and set out on his journey.

He had not gone very far when he was joined by the old woman who reprimanded him for not taking her advice. She told him she was grateful for his kindness and decided to follow him. 'When I saw you enter the Inn, I knew you were in great danger. The fact they knew that I had seen you prevented you from being killed.' He thanked her for the protection and continued on his way, grateful to be one of the lucky ones. Unfortunately reports of travellers disappearing continued for many years after.

Legend prefers to report that Cap Coch died peacefully in 1820 at the grand old age of ninety surrounded by his acquired wealth. Historical facts show, however, that he was hanged at Stalling Downs, near Cowbridge, on a charge of stealing a sheep.

In 1826 the main bridge to the town centre was constructed over the River Ogmore. The New Inn's activities were curtailed and soon it fell into decay until eventually it was demolished in the early 1900's. Only then did the grisly truth emerge. Behind one side of the panelled kitchen wall was found a smugglers' hole and some of Cap Coch's ill gained booty. A dig of the garden revealed far more sinister finds. There buried in every conceivable place — in two's and three's like a churchyard — were the bodies of missing travellers. A search of the fields and woods behind the New Inn revealed even more skeletons. It was believed Cap Coch, being concerned of the rumours about the bodies in the River Ogmore decided to dispose of his victims in a safer place away from the inn.

Iolo Morganwg's Love of Glamorgan

The National Eisteddfod and the white robed bardic rituals of Wales are well known throughout Wales and further afield. This ceremonial gathering of musicians, poets and craftsmen take place in the first week of August at a site announced with elaborate ritual a year and a day before. Most people believe these ancient customs date back to the Druids, who were tribal priests during the time of the Roman invasion. But they actually originated in the fertile mind of one Glamorgan man, Iolo Morganwg. His name is well known to every Welsh historian, not always for his great academic abilities but as a notorious forger of old manuscripts.

Iolo's great love for his county became such an obsession he set out to prove it was the home of the bardic traditions of the Druids by fabricating old tales, genealogies and records. He even composed triads and poems and developed the theory about early Eisteddfodau and bardic ceremonies, declaring he had found the material in old Glamorgan manuscripts. Most famous of all Iolo's fabrications are the *cywyddau* — odes — which he wrote himself, but blatantly attributed to the great Welsh poet Dafydd ap Gwilym who lived in the 14th century. These he called *Cywyddau'r Ychwanegiad* — additional poems.

Iolo Morganwg was born Edward Williams, in 1746 at Penon, a hamlet adjoining the parish of Llancarfan. His parents moved to Flemingston and Iolo spent most of his life in the locality surrounded by its interesting traditions and historical background. His father was a stone-mason and his mother, daughter of a gentleman named Matthew, was a well educated woman who was interested in literature. From an early age, Iolo learnt stone-masonry but always maintained his heart was never in business, only in books. He was a delicate child who, until his mother's death when he was still young, was taught at home. Then, like most children of the day, he furthered his knowledge in the rules of grammar and poetic art from the bards and literary men of the county.

About 1772 Iolo left for London to make an independent living for himself. His sudden departure is explained in an interesting story in which it would appear that the village parsonage was being altered by Mr Williams and his sons. One day, instead of going for his dinner break with the others, Iolo remained behind on his own to eat and read his books. Before leaving, his father warned, 'Now my boy, take care of the house, and keep out the pigs and poultry. The servants are at dinner too so we are relying on you to look after the house'. Iolo promised, but once alone became so absorbed in his books that when his father returned he found his son sitting on the green outside the house, oblivious to the chaos around him. Pigs, fowls and ducks had made themselves at home thoughout the house, a calf had taken possession of the kitchen and a donkey was taking a rest in the parlour. Iolo deeply resented his father's anger particularly as he had never wanted to follow in the family trade, favouring instead his beloved books. He hastily packed his satchel full of books, walked out and nothing was heard of him for about three months. Eventually he wrote to say he was employed dressing stone for Blackfriars Bridge.

At this time the Welsh writers and poets living in London formed societies for the study of Welsh literature. Here Iolo met and conversed with people such as Owain Myfyr, William Owen Pughe and others. He read old manuscripts, copied the poems of Dafydd ap Gwilym and often contributed to Welsh and English publications.

Another interesting story tells of Iolo's first meeting with Prime Minister William Pitt who had heard about Iolo's talents as a bard and expressed a wish to meet him. One evening, without an invitation, Iolo arrived at the Minister's door asking to see him. The footman, having informed his master that a poorly dressed man was at the door was told to tell the stranger he was too busy to see him. Iolo insisted and, on hearing this, Pitt grabbed his whip and hurried to the door. Iolo burst into an impromptu verse, and greeted the Minister reciting:

'Strike a Welshman if you dare
Ancient Briton though we are;

We were men of great renown
Ere a Saxon wore a crown!'

Immediately Pitt exclaimed, 'The Welsh bard, come in, come in'. Dressed as he was, Iolo was invited to join a party that was under way and delighted everyone with his knowledge and conversational abilities.

As a member of the Gwyneddigion Society of London he was hearing continually the praises of the bards of Gwynedd and the traditions of North Wales. He was concerned that North Wales received all the praise and thought South Wales, especially Glamorgan, had so much culture to offer. So his obsession to prove his county great began.

In 1773 Iolo moved to Dartford in Kent and became a frequent contributor to *Town and County Magazine*, the *Monthly Magazine* and the *Gentleman's Magazine*. All the money he received for these contributions he spent on books to further his knowledge. In 1777 he returned to London, but after only a short while, went home to Glamorgan and wrote the following poem:

'No more of London's hateful noise,
    Ye madden'd crowds, adien;
Detested arts, ungenial joys,
I dwell no more with you.

Hail! dear Glamorgan, let me greet
    Once more the favour'd plain,
I fly with gladden'd soul to greet
My native cot again.'

Iolo continued to work as a stone mason and also on his literary compositions and researches. However, in 1781 he married and the demands of a young family curtailed his literary contributions.

In the summer of 1792 Iolo, with a group of London based Welshmen, held the first Gorsedd meeting at Primrose Hill in North London. These semi-Christian, semi-mystical rituals had taken place, successfully, in North Wales, but now with renewed interest in Welsh culture the practice caught on in South Wales too. Thanks to much persuasion by Iolo it was eventually incorporated into the National Eisteddfod. At this time, Iolo's theories were readily accepted by Welsh historians who were completely taken in by his claims concerning the origins of ceremonies such as *Gorsedd Beirdd Ynys Prydain* — The Gorsedd of the Bards of the Isle of Britain.

In 1797 he ceased working as a stone mason because inhaling the fine dust made worse his asthma. To try and support his family, he opened a shop in Cowbridge where he sold books, stationary and groceries. He was not a successful bookseller, but had many other occupations including surveying South Wales for the Board of Agriculture and drawing a geological map of Glamorgan.

According to records Iolo was a very eccentric looking man with long grey hair underneath a tall beaver hat. He wore a blue coat with brass buttons, and a pair of well worn corduroy breeches. He was very fond of walking and wore a pair of stout shoes with ornamented silver buckles. He was often seen trudging along the country lanes with a pair of canvas type wallets slung across his shoulders. These contained a change of linen and a variety of books and papers connected with whatever he was researching at that time. As he walked he would carry a notebook, and with his pencil poised between his fingers was ready to jot down any idea that came to mind.

He was often accompanied by a horse who would follow him like an obedient dog. Sometimes the pair would walk to Cardiff where they would stop at a baker's shop. Iolo would buy a loaf of bread and fed it to his four footed friend broken into pieces. Once the animal was fed and watered, Iolo would go into a friend's house for tea, his favourite beverage, while the animal waited patiently outside. The horse had been given to Iolo by a friend who was concerned at the long distances he covered on foot. Iolo, although devoted to the horse, refused to ride it. He had only ridden once before in his life and never forgot the experience. On that occasion, on hearing of his father's sudden illness, in his rush to visit he had forgotten to saddle the horse, and the memory of the effect had remained with him for the rest of his life.

For all his eccentricities, he was indisputable a man of

remarkable ability, and contributed much to discovering and preserving Welsh culture. No less than seventy-five volumes of his work can be found in the Llanover collection of manuscripts today.

In 1826 he died and was buried in Flemingston churchyard in the vale he loved so much. A commemorative plaque has been placed on the house in Cowbridge where, for a short time, he lived and worked as a bookseller. On his tombstone can be found a most fitting inscription:

In Memory
of
EDWARD WILLIAMS
(Iolo Morganwg)
of the village
Stone mason, Bard, Antiquary

Born in Penon in the adjoining parish of
Llancarvan, on the 19th March, 1746.
Died on the 18th day of December, 1826.

'His remains are deposited near this spot. His mind was stored with the histories and traditions of Wales. He studied nature too in all her works. His mortal part was weak, and rendered him little able to ply trade, but God endorsed him with mental faculties, patience of research, and vigor of intellect, which were not clouded by his humble occupation. He was never at school, yet he became a large contributor of acknowledged authority to bardic and historic literature. His simple habits, cheerful manners, and varied knowledge made him a welcome visitor within the mansions of the rich as well as the cottages of the poor, and many there are who will still have a kindly recollection of him. By these and others who appreciate his genius this tablet was erected A.D. 1855. He feared God and walked meekly and uprightly with his fellowmen.'

The Legend of Southerndown Common

Ask any native of Southerndown, a small seaside village near Ogmore on Sea, about Southerndown Common and you are liable to be corrected. They will promptly answer that you mean '*Satterdown*', and then quickly recount the story concerning the Welsh heroine they are so proud of.

Sometime during the 12th century, Maurice de Londres, son of the builder of nearby Ogmore castle, left his favourite seat at Kidwelly to live at Ogmore. He was a great sportsman and, with a group of friends, enjoyed hunting the stags which roamed freely in the forests surrounding the castle.

The Welsh, who were the rightful owners of the land on which the castle was built, were forbidden to hunt or kill the animals. As this was the chief source of food with which they supported themselves and their families, life became increasingly difficult for them, and many took the risk of killing a stag in the hope that they would not be caught. These were cruel times, and anyone found breaking the law would have their eyes burnt out in public with red hot irons.

One day a Welshman, reputed to be a chief or prince, was caught red-handed with bow posed in hand having just killed a deer. He was pounced upon by de Londres' men, bound hand and foot and taken to the castle to await his punishment.

The following morning, at sunrise, Sir Maurice and his men went into the great courtyard where the villagers had gathered to witness the public humiliation. The red hot embers were glowing and the irons almost ready to inflict their barbaric punishment.

As the red-haired prisoner and his torturer were led into the courtyard the Welsh crowd fell silent. The prisoner looked rebelliously around the crowd until his eyes met the tired but beautiful face of his wife, who was clutching a young baby to her breast. His eyes, full of sadness, glanced down at the ground as his bottom lip quivered. We can only surmise what went through this man's mind knowing this would be the last time he'd see his wife and child.

Watching this spectacle alongside Sir Maurice was his daughter who, it is reputed, had many friends and admirers among the Welsh. Looking from husband to wife her heart must have been filled with compassion for the couple. She threw herself at her father's feet reminding him it was her birthday. As a special birthday present she asked her father to spare the prisoner's eyes.

Sir Maurice hesitated, then remembered that on this day years ago he had experienced a sad event. His dearly loved wife had lost her life giving birth to his daughter. Full of sympathy the Lord of Ogmore relented and granted his daughter her wish.

Then, trying her luck further, she reminded her father that the land on which he enjoyed hunting rightfully belonged to the Welsh and he should return to them a common area on which they could kill animals and live in peace and security. At first her father hesitated but his daughter continued to smile at him. Eventually he agreed.

'Granted, my daughter,' he said, 'But on one condition'.

'Anything, anything you wish father,' cried the young woman, jumping to her feet and dancing around him in delight.

'Your Welsh friends shall have all the land that you can walk round bare-footed and alone from now until sunset'.

The shocked crowd begged that she be allowed sandals to protect her feet, but her father refused, believing footwear would make the task too easy and allow more ground to be recovered for the Welsh. Immediately the daughter removed her footwear, flung them defiantly to the ground, and set out up a long steep and stony trackway, which today still leads from Ogmore Castle to the hills above. Over rough and smooth ground the brave girl tramped. Flinging aside prickly gorse and thorny bramble bushes she pressed on, her path identified by blood stained stones, until the sun was setting in the west and sinking into the sea.

Finally the Welsh heroine, worn and hungry, her feet torn and bleeding, 'sat her down' on a stone above the king's woods. Thus winning for the Welsh the land which has been known for centuries as Southerndown Common.

Tales of Old Dunraven

Dunraven Castle near Southerndown, was inhabited by the princes of Glamorgan from the earliest times until Iestyn ap Gwrgan. It is said that Caradog or Caractacus, the old Welsh chieftain who brought christianity to Wales, and his father *Brân ap Llŷr* — Brân the blessed, also lived here. At the time of Christ's birth, Cynfelyn, an uncle of Brân ap Llŷr ruled part of Glamorgan, and a meadow near Dunraven is still called Maesmelyn, or field or Cynfelyn.

Eventually Dunraven became the home of the Botteler, or Butler family, one of the Norman Knights who served under William de Londres. He was also one of Robert Fitzhamon's comrades on the invasion of Glamorgan. During the early part of the 16th century the male line of the Butler family were wiped out and, through marriage of a surviving daughter, Dunraven went to a prominent family in the days of the Tudor dynasty, the Vaughan's of Carmarthenshire.

Dunraven, which is derived from the Welsh *Dindryfan*, meaning a triangular fortress, was still standing until earlier this century. Following a dispute between the owner who wished to develop it and the local authority who refused permission, the owner demolished it and little remains today.

However there are many legendary tales about Dunraven castle mostly involving the Vaughan family. One of the most interesting is a true story, although how much legend has been embroidered into the historical tapestry is unknown. However, we do know that Walter Vaughan, Lord Dunraven had four sons, all of whom died in tragic circumstances.

One day Vaughan, on seeing a ship on the dangerous rocks below the castle swam out to the wreck and, with the aid of a rope, saved many lives. He was so shocked by the incident that he devised a sea rescue plan which he submitted to the government. Unfortunately they did not take him seriously and would not consider his scheme. Vaughan, who was a well respected man, was so outraged and embittered by this rejection that it changed his personality. Soon he was spending money recklessly and this made for a poor family life. His wife, saddened by his changed personality and unable to cope, died of a broken heart. She left him with four sons, the youngest only four years old. His eldest, and favourite son, seeing his inheritance disappearing deserted his father, and inspired by people like Sir Walter Raleigh and the Spanish Armada decided to begin a new life abroad and hopefully make enough money to save the family honour.

Vaughan's wild spending had led him to the verge of bankruptcy and when another ship was wrecked he, as Lord of the Manor, claimed it to be his. The ship yielded much wealth and saved him. This gave him an idea to help his finances further. Locals had long had the reputation of deliberately wrecking ships for their own gain. To confuse the sailors at sea and thus lure the ships onto the dangerous rocks they placed lanterns on sheep and oxen horns as they grazed in the fields above the sea. Vaughan decided to enlist the wreckers help and strike up a wrecking partnership.

The wrecker's leader, known locally as *Matt of the Iron Hand*, had been a captain of a pirate ship. Many years before his ship was seized by the authorities and Vaughan, then a respectable local magistrate, had given the order for it to be impounded. In the struggle that followed Matt's hand was cut off by a knife, later to be replaced by an iron hook fastened to the stump of his arm — hence the nickname. Perhaps Vaughan had forgotten about this incident or believed Matt would not harbour a grudge. A partnership was agreed and the wrecking business began to prosper. However, it was a mistake that was to cost Vaughan dear when fate showed her evil hand.

One bright sunny day, two of Vaughan's sons set out to sea on a fishing trip in the calm waters of the bay. Suddenly an unexpected storm blew up and drove their craft onto the rugged rocks. Vaughan rushed from the castle but had to watch helplessly as his sons met their deaths. Further tragedy was to hit the Vaughan household. When the servants rushed from the castle to try to attempt a rescue they left the youngest son asleep in the castle. The child woke thirsty and, in trying to get a drink, fell into a vessel of whey and drowned. Vaughan was deeply shocked by these events. He regarded them as retribution for his evil deeds and tried to make amends. By now he was getting old and wished only that his favourite son would return home so that they could be reconciled. Servants at the castle said that Vaughan spent most of his time looking out to sea watching for a foreign ship that would bring his wandering son home. But his final punishment was yet to come.

One day a terrible storm lashed the Glamorgan coast and Vaughan saw a ship trying to find temporary shelter in an inlet. It was getting dark and Matt put out his false lights to lure the ship to its doom. Amid the wind and the waves the crew realised that they were heading for the rocks. They tried desperately to steer clear but failed. Finally they abandoned ship and swam towards the beach, but only one man survived.

It was a rule among the wreckers that no sailor should survive to be a court witness if any of the gang were caught. Matt, as leader, approached the exhausted swimmer, who turned out to be the ship's captain. He pleaded with Matt to spare his life, saying that he was a Welshman and a native of Dunraven. Despite his pleas Matt coldly bludgeoned the sailor to death but, no sooner had he done so, he recognised the captain and Matt's evil eyes lit up. He reached down and, with one swift slice of his knife, cut off the sailor's hand.

Meanwhile, on the cliff top, Vaughan was watching the killing, and felt remorse for the life that had just ended on the beach below him. After a short while Matt approached him waving the murdered man's bloody hand. On one of the fingers Vaughan saw the distinctive ring he had given his eldest son many years ago. Slowly his disbelief turned to terror as he realised the full extent of what had happened.

Broken hearted at the death of his son, Vaughan quickly disposed of the property to John Wyndham, Serjeant-at-Law, whose memorial and bust is preserved at St Brides Major church. He then fled from Dunraven never to be heard of in the country again.

As for Matt, some say he was shot by a faithful servant or villager, whilst others claim he was hung a few months later for the murder of another ship wrecked sailor. Whatever the truth, Matt certainly got his revenge on the tragic Vaughan family.

The Wreckers of Rhosili

The South Glamorgan coast was not the only area to play host to the wicked wreckers. Rhosili, on the Gower Peninsula had its organised gangs too. One gang operated their lucrative business by luring ships up the Channel, past Lundy, towards Worms Head where the ships would be pounded to pieces on the rocks. Any unsuspecting Captain peering into the darkness would see a light, which they would assume was a safe port. The 'safe port' often turned out to be a child walking back and forth with a lantern hung on a cow horn to simulate a ship heading for port.

There are many tales about these wreckers, but the saddest story concerns a young orphan girl called Kate. It made such an impression on people that the tale is now preserved in ballad form by J.M. Neale (1818-1866), a scholar and hymnologist.

On Easter Day 1712, the whole of the south coast was lashed with violent storms, giving the wreckers in both areas an ideal opportunity to commit their evil deeds. That evening, at the *Goat Inn* which sadly has disappeared, the Rhosili wreckers gathered to plan their nights work.

Kate, a fourteen year old girl, had been sent from the local orphanage to work for them. She was poorly dressed and often treated cruelly by the men. In return for her food and shelter she carried the lantern over the cliffs. It is recorded that she remained unmoved by the sounds of the crashing timbers and the haunting screams of the sailors as their ships were hit against the rocks. It was all in a night's work to her and she knew that a bowl of soup and a bed awaited her return.

Although she was illiterate, the wreckers allowed her to attend the local church, where she learned to repeat the Creed and the

Lord's Prayer parrot fashion. Often, in his sermons, the rector would condemn the evil deeds of the wreckers but his words had little or no effect on the majority of people because they enjoyed sharing the spoils from the wrecked ships. After many such sermons his words finally played on Kate's conscience and, just before the Easter storm, she decided she would have no more to do with the wreckers activities.

On this particular night, as she sat besides the men in the *Goat Inn*, she heard the only too familiar words. 'Kate, there's a ship heading for the bay. Don't waste time. Here's the lantern. You know what you must do.' She hesitated thinking of the Rector's last sermon, but one of the men pulled her to her feet, and spoke sharply. 'Now on with your cape and hat, there's a good girl.'

'Oh, pity her on the high hillside,
So little to help her, so little to guide,
So feeble a light to make things clear,
So little to hope and so much to fear,
For if she returned to the Rhosili men,
And the ship rode safe on the sea, what then?
Her life was nought to that smuggling crew
If the thing they ordered she failed to do.

A few of the wreckers protested saying that with such a high wind blowing it was no night for a young girl to be out but she was pushed, lantern in hand, through the door into the jaws of a gale force storm.

Fighting against the wind and rain Kate made her way along the dangerous rocky causeway and was soon standing on the cliff-top of Worms Head. She had been taught to walk almost to the end of the cliffs before lighting the lantern. Then she would come slowly to the edge, swinging the lantern from side to side until the wreckers, watching from Rhosili Downs, fired a gun to indicate that her mission was completed. If the tide permitted, she would return across the narrow causeway which separated Worms Head from the mainland, but more often than not she was forced to find shelter and remain on the Head until the tide receded.

Kate heard the ship below. The Rector's words echoed in her mind and she knew that, whatever the consequences, she could not lead another unsuspecting ship to its doom. Nearby was a pile of brushwood, kept in case a beacon was needed. Placing the unlit lantern in a crevice in the rocks, she stripped the furze from the brushwood and lit it. Within a few moments, the wind had fanned a great fire. From the reflected glow, the Captain managed to take his bearings and soon the ship was speeding out into the Channel towards Cardiff docks.

Kate never returned to Rhosili and a few days later her body was washed ashore, some say with a large gash on her forehead. Others told of seeing her slip and fall into the rough seas as she negotiated the rocks on her way home. Being an orphan, there was no one to really care what happened to Kate, so no enquiries were made and she was buried immediately.

This is where Kate's story should have ended, but many years later an old man dying of a fever in Carmarthen jail provided the missing link in the puzzle. He kept calling for Kate and, although delirious, the prison chaplain managed to piece together what had happened on that fateful Easter night of 1712.

Kate had managed to save the vessel, but the wreckers were furious. Mad with rage they raced across the downs and over the causeway raving and shouting abuse at the girl. In the struggle that followed one man, Bill Williams, swung a boathook and struck the girl on the forehead. Kate died instantly. The dying man was anxious to tell the Chaplain that, although he played no part in her murder, he had been guilty of helping to throw her frail body into the raging sea.

The sun went down over Rhosili Bay —
    And a dying shriek
Was heard in the creek
As life was flung to the angry sea.

If you visit Rhosili today you will be able to see for yourself how dangerous Worms Head can become. Take note of the tides though, because many people have been marooned on the Head until the causeway is safe to cross once more.

In St Mary's parish churchyard is an area with no gravestones. It is believed to be the unmarked graves of unknown sailors who perished at the hands of the wicked wreckers.

How the Old Parish got it's Name

The old village of Llangynwyd, near Maesteg in Mid Glamorgan sits neatly between the hills, and is just one mile west of the modern village of Llangynwyd. The name probably derives from its connection with the old Tir Iarll, or Earl's land, when it formed part of the estate belonging to the first Norman conquerors of Glamorgan. However, locally the old village will always be known as Yr Hen Blwyf — the Old Parish. Ask any villager the reason and they are only too willing to retell the story behind its name.

One day a local carpenter was asked to make a coffin for a man who had died at the age of twenty-eight but, being uneducated he had no idea how to write the figure 28. Deeply perplexed and worried he began to count on his fingers and think of all the numbers that he did know. The more he tried, the more confused he became. Finally he took his boots off and counted his toes, but still he had no idea how to form the required figures. Suddenly a spark of inspiration flashed through his mind. At last he had found a solution to his problem. He remembered that four sevens add up to 28 and, as he knew how to write the figure 7, he decided to put down four sevens in a row — 7777 — and trust that people would understand what he meant.

On the day of the burial the clergyman was taken ill, so a stranger to the area was called in to conduct the service. When he saw the inscription etched on the coffin he was amazed, but decided to say nothing. During the service he was informed by the relatives that the man had spent all his life in the same parish. 'Duw', exclaimed the cleric. 'This must indeed be a very old parish.' And from that day onwards, Llangynwyd became known by that name.

However, Llangynwyd has its tragic tale too. It dates back to the 18th century and is encircled with an air of romance. The story goes that Ann Thomas of Cafyndfa was betrothed by her mother, to Anthony Maddoc, a well respected young lawyer, and son of a wealthy local family. Unfortunately she had fallen in love with Will Hopkin, the local poet and thatcher and wanted to marry him. Despite her pleas Ann's mother felt that Will was not good enough for her daughter, and insisted she marry Anthony Maddoc. Will, it is said, left the area brokenhearted. The wedding took place in 1725, and Ann and Anthony had a daughter who died in infancy. Two years later Will returned to find Ann insane and on the point of death. With her mother's and husband's blessing, Ann died in Will's arms from, it is claimed, a broken heart.

Will, unable to forget his love for Ann never married. He died some fourteen years later when he fell from a ladder whilst thatching a roof. It is said that the famous song *'Bugeilio'r Gwenith Gwyn'* — Watching the Wheat — was written by him as he sought relief by pouring out his feelings for Ann in poetic energy. The English translation goes something like this:

A simple youthful swain am I
Who loves at fancy's pleasure;
I fondly watch the blooming wheat,
Another reaps the treasure
O! wherefore still despite the suit,
Why pining keep thy lover?
For some new charm, thou matchless fair,
I day by day discover.

When Welshmen left their native land to explore and settle in foreign lands, they took this song with them, helping to carry the tale of Will's enormous love for Ann throughout the world.

How much of this story is legend and how much fact we do not know. Ann certainly existed as her marriage contract is still preserved and her burial place is marked by a stone in the chancel of the local church. In 1735 we know Will took part in an Eisteddfod at Cymer and his body is reputed to be buried near a yew tree in the local churchyard. No commemoration exists but a modern stone has been erected outside the churchyard in memory of Will and other celebrities.

Birth of an Anthem

The heart of every true Welshman must fill with *'hiraeth'* — a longing - whenever he hears the beautiful melody of the National Anthem *'Hen Wlad Fy Nhadau,'* — Land of my Fathers. But the story behind its composition is fascinating.

It was composed in 1856 by Evan James and his son James who lived in the small village of Pontypridd in the Rhondda Valley. Evan was a weaver living at Argoed in Gwent when James was born and the family moved to Pontypridd when Evan took over a small woollen factory.

James, who never enjoyed the family tradition of attending church services on a Sunday evening, had became quite an expert at dreaming up excuses not to go. As his mother was preparing for church one bitterly cold winter's night, James told her he did not feel very well and asked if he could be excused. His mother agreed but, as soon as his parents had left, he dressed for the weather and took a stroll along the local river — The Taff.

As he walked slowly along the banks the sound of the steady flow of water inspired him to compose a melody. When he stopped to watch the water thundering and cascading along he thought of the famous battles of the past, the bravery of the Welsh as they fought hard, their blood spilling over the land of their fathers as they fought to keep it free. As the water slowed and flowed majestically along, he thought of the lyrical poetry and the national songs of his beloved country. When the moonlight glistened on the clear water, he thought of the beauty that surrounded him in the rolling hills, the lush green valleys and the rugged coastline and the crashing waves against the rocks.

By the time he arrived back at his humble home, the tune for 'Land of My Fathers', was racing through his head. He pulled off his coat and immediately sat down to write the score. When his father returned from church he showed the music to him and tol_ him he had faked illness to walk along the river bank and that the sounds of the water had inspired him to write the melody. His father was so proud that he sat down and wrote the first verse that evening.

The second and third verses were completed during the following week and they gave it the title 'Glan Rhondda' — The Banks of The Rhondda — to commemorate where it had been composed.

Evan and James entered their composition in the National Eisteddfod at Llangollen in 1858 and were delighted to be awarded a prize and a medal.

Unfortunately, in spite of its resounding success, the song was not taken seriously by the Welsh people. Three years after it was composed it was included in an anthology of Welsh melodies, and given the title of 'Hen Wlad Fy Nhadau' — Land of My Fathers — from the first line of the anthem. Naturally it was first sung by a Welsh congregation in the James' home town of Pontypridd and, by the end of the century, became recognised as the Welsh National Anthem.

The Welsh people were very proud of their father and son team, and in 1909 set up a national fund to honour them. Every Welshman and woman was encouraged to contribute and, by 1914, the fund had reached a record total of £1,000 — a considerable amount in those days.

It was decided to erect, in Ynysangharad park, Pontypridd, statues of a woman to represent poetry, and a man holding a harp to symbolise music. The memorial was designed by Sir W. Goscombe John R.A. but the project had to be abandoned when the First World War was declared. War was followed by depression but eventually in 1930 the statues were unveiled at a wonderful occasion attended by over 10,000 Welsh people singing the words to the accompaniment of the band of the Fifth Welsh Regiment.

Today you can see the original manuscript of the words and music of 'Hen Wlad Fy Nhadau' in the National Library at

Aberystwyth in mid-Wales. A tablet on a house in Mill Street, Ponypridd marks the James' former residence.

Shelley's Tragic Dash to Swansea

Many famous literary people have visited Glamorgan, but none with such a sad mission as one of our greatest romantic poets, Percy Bysshe Shelley.

It all began on the morning of Wednesday, 9th October 1816 when his wife Mary received a most distressing letter. She showed it to Percy who gasped in horror and immediately prepared himself for the long arduous journey to South Wales. First he would have to travel from London to Bristol where he would board the Cambrian Coach for the final part of the journey to Swansea.

At this time highwaymen were very active along the coach routes and we can imagine Shelley would have become quite agitated on the journey. Certainly he would not want any delays by highwaymen or through muddy flooded roadways. We can only assume that he prayed during his journey that his hurried departure would not be in vain.

Meanwhile, on the very same Wednesday evening as Shelley's coach was trundling along the earthy highways, a smartly dressed young lady disembarked from the previous Cambrian Coach at Swansea and booked into the fashionable Mackworth Arms. After light refreshments she retired to bed informing the chambermaid that she wished not to be disturbed because she was extremely tired and needed a long rest.

The following morning the young lady failed to appear for breakfast and, after much deliberation, the management forced the bedroom door only to find her dead, a bottle of laudanum and a suicide note on the table beside the bed.

Shelley, still aboard the coach making its way to Swansea, was sadly unaware of the tragic event at the Mackworth that he was so desperately trying to prevent.

The Friday, 11th October, 1816 edition of the local newspaper,

The Cambrian, carried the following extract, interesting for its clear details of the fashions of the day.

"A melancholy discovery was made in Swansea yesterday. A most respectable looking female arrived at the Mackworth Arms on Wednesday night by the Cambrian Coach from Bristol. She took tea, retired to rest, telling the chambermaid that she was exceedingly fatigued and would take care of the candle herself. Much agitation was created in the house by her non appearance yesterday morning, and on forcing her chamber door she was found a corpse with the remains of a bottle of laudanum on the table and a note.

The name appears to have been torn off and burnt, but her stockings are marked with the letter G, and on her stays the letters M.W. are visible. She was dressed in a blue striped skirt with a white body, and a brown pelice, with a fur trimming of a lighter colour, lined with white silk, and a hat of the same. She had a small French gold watch, and appears about 23 years of age, with long brown hair, dark complexion and a reticule containing a red silk pocket handkerchief, a brown-berry necklace, and a small leather clasped purse containing three shillings, and five shillings and six penny pieces.

She told a fellow traveller that she came from Bath by the mail from London on Tuesday morning from whence to Swansea by the Cambrian Coach. We hope the description we have given of this unhappy catastrophe will lead to the discovery of the wretched object who has prematurely closed her existance."

Who was this respectable young woman with the letter G and M.W. worked into her clothes? Would they hold the key to her identity? And where did Shelley fit into this mystery? These were the questions that must have been asked by the authorities. The woman's suicide note certainly did not throw any light on the matter, although it revealed clearly her state of mind at the time of her untimely death. It read as follows:-

"I have long determined that the best thing I could do was to put an end to the existence of the being whose birth was unfortunate, and whose life has only been a series of pain to the persons who have hurt their health in endeavouring to promote her welfare. Perhaps to hear of my death will give you pain, but you will soon have the blessing of forgetting that such a creature existed as . . . ''

Eventually it emerged that the young woman who had committed suicide was Fanny Imlay, half-sister to Mary Shelley, and a sad dejected victim of circumstance.

Her father, Gilbert Imlay, was a captain in the American War of Independence. In 1793 he went to live with Mary Wollstonecroft, firstly in Le Havre and then London, but 18 months later left her with their baby daughter, Fanny. Later that same year Mary married William Godwin but died five months later giving birth to her second daughter, Mary, later to become Shelley's wife. Godwin, alone with two young daughters, married a widow with a family , and they spent the rest of their days in poverty in Skinner Street, Swansea.

When Shelley finally arrived in Swansea, Fanny was already dead. Distressed at being too late to save his sister-in-law and, after reading Fanny's last sad words, he recalled his last meeting with her in London and wrote a touching poem:

Her voice did quiver as we parted
Yet knew I not that heart was broken
From which it came, and I departed
Heeding not the words then spoken
Misery — O Misery
This world is all too wide for thee.

A most fitting epitaph following a tragic incident and one that shows the sensitivity of Shelley.

The Legends of King Arthur's Stone

Just ten miles from the City of Swansea, sitting proud and erect on Cefn Bryn, that rugged backbone of Gower, Coeten Arthur or Arthur's stone reigns majestically encircled by its legendary tales and customs. To the uninformed it is just another large grey boulder, but to the informed it is a mysterious stone, surrounded with magical myths, and a history that reaches back into the deep mists of the Neolithic period. It's origins are not known, but it is thought to be a chambered burial tomb or cromlech, dating from approximately 2500 B.C. However, some historians believe it to be the Maen (stone) Cetti, one of the seven wonders of the Ancient world.

King Arthur's stone is capped with a boulder weighing some 25 tons, with a number of smaller stones scattered around. An impressive stone of this size suggest it was covered with an earthen mound, now long since vanished, and was once the burial ground of an important person. Curiously, the space below is not sufficiently large for a body and personal possessions and no bones have been found.

Immediately below the cromlech is a spring of clear water or holy well. We know from historians that, in their superstitious beliefs, the Druids consecrated rocks, caves and lakes so perhaps King Arthur's stone was erected over a hallowed well renown for its healing powers.

Whatever its purpose, it is surrounded by legends. It is believed that, because the stone contains specks of red sandstone, similar to bloodstains, it was used during the Druid Iron Age as a sacrificial alter for human sacrifice.

A piece appears to have been sliced off the main capstone, confirmed in records to have occurred before the end of the 17th century. Legend has many explanations for this. One states the stone was struck by a bolt of lightening whilst another that a local miller split it when he was looking for a suitable millstone. Yet another states that during the 6th century, Dewi Sant, St David, the patron Saint of Wales, fearing a return of Druidism and the worshipping of pagan gods, struck the stone with his staff and split it, proving that it was an alter to the false gods.

The stone takes its name from the legendary King Arthur who, in about 539 AD, was passing through Carmarthenshire on his way to the battle of Camlon when he was troubled by a pebble in his shoe. He stopped, removed the pebble, and threw it as far as he could. Legend states it landed on Cefn Bryn, some seven miles

away, where it grew to enormous proportions. It appears that the stone is quite mobile too. It is claimed that on Midsummer's Eve, the stone takes a trip down to the shore of the Burry estuary for a drink of water.

There is also a delightful old custom that at midnight when there was a full moon, young maidens would test their lovers fidelity by making a cake of barleymeal and honey which was wetted with milk before being kneaded on the stone. The girl would crawl around the stone three times on all fours. If her young man appeared, it proved he was faithful and wished to marry her. If not he never intended to marry her. The girls believed that some magical power from within the stone drew her lover to the stone, but I suspect that if he really wanted to marry he would have made an arrangment for the girls mother to let him know when the test would take place.

A visit to King Arthur's stone is a must for any visitor to South Wales. Even in the fifteenth century it was recognised as an ancient wonder and had become a famous 'tourist' attraction. Records show that when the Breton troops in Henry VII's army landed at Mill Bay, St Anne's head in Pembrokeshire, en route to Bosworth Field, they made a detour of some eighty miles to see the stone.

The Baglan Giant saved by a pair of boots

Once upon a time in the old village of Baglan, two miles from Swansea, a conceited giant named Hywel lived in a mountainside cottage with his wife. He enjoyed boasting that he feared no one in the world because he was the strongest and most powerful giant in Wales. His bragging annoyed the villagers and they dreaded meeting him, because he would always challenge them to a fight. Feelings became so bad that people made lengthy detours around the mountain to avoid the egotistical man.

At the same time, in Ireland, there lived a giant feared by everyone because they thought he was the strongest, tallest and most powerful man in the world. When he heard about him Hywel challenged the Irishman to a duel thinking the Irishman had better things to do than cross the water and fight him. At least that is what he hoped.

Weeks, then months passed and Hywel heard nothing from the Irishman. Assuming his theory was correct, Hywel began to boast that even the strongest man in the world was afraid to accept his challenge. There was no stopping him and everyone hoped that one day Hywel would meet his match, if only to stop him from bragging.

Then one glorious summer's day, as he was sitting outside his cottage smoking his clay pipe and admiring the view, he looked down the mountain and was horrified to see the Irish giant taking large strides towards the house. Hywel, who was really very timid when faced with a challenge, was terrified and dashed into the house and, clinging to his wife's apron, begged her to help him. His wife thought hard for a moment and then she said she had a plan but could not guarantee it would work.

'Anything, anything,' begged Hywel. 'Just try to save me from this frightful giant.'

She made Hywel take off his three-foot long boots and put them at the side of the fire-place. Then she pointed to the stairs.

'Now go to bed, and do not make a sound or come down until I call you.'

In minutes the Irish giant arrived and hammered on the front door demanding Hywel to come out and fight. Hywel's wife flung open the door and told the giant to be quiet because her baby son was asleep upstairs.

'Where's Hywel the giant?' he demanded. 'I have come to challenge him to a duel.'

'He's just slipped out for a moment', said Hywel's wife. 'He won't be long though, and I know he is so looking forward to meeting and fighting this duel with you. Come inside and sit down, but please be quiet or you will wake my baby, and it has taken me ages to get him to sleep.'

The giant stepped into the house and, looking around

suspiciously, glanced down at the boots on the hearth. Pointing to the boots he bellowed.

'If your husband is out as you say, then who may I ask are these?' lifting the boots from the ground.

'Oh those,' laughed Hywel's wife. 'Duw, fancy you thinking those tiny things were my husband's. They are my baby's bootees, although they won't be for much longer. I was only saying to Hywel this morning, that the lad has already grown out of them.'

The Irish giant turned pale, dropped the boots to the ground and staggered from the house and down the path.

'Oh', he managed to gulp at last as he turned to face Hywel's wife. 'I have suddenly remembered, I have some urgent business in Ireland, and must leave immediately. Perhaps I can meet your husband some other time.'

Then the Irishman dashed down the mountain as fast as his legs could carry him and fled to his awaiting boat back to Ireland. Legend tells us the two giants never met again. When he was safely away from their mountainside home Hywel's wife called her husband from the bedroom and, because he was so grateful that his wife had saved him, he never boasted of his power and strength again.

The Legends of Tresilian Cave

The ancient castle of St Donat's stands on the most southerly coast of Wales overlooking the Bristol Channel. It was inhabited by the Stradling family from the 13th century when Peter de Stradling, a Swiss Knight, married Joan de Hawey, a Norman heiress.

Just below the castle is the secluded haven of Tresilian Bay — the place of Silian where it is reputed Prince Silian kept court during the 3rd and 4th centuries. He was one of the first pagans to be converted to Christianity and, after his death, became a saint. St. Silian's court eventually was replaced by an Inn which, because of its convenient location, became a favourite haunt of smugglers and wreckers. On the western side of this site lies a huge cave which was used by the smugglers and is believed to lead to St Donat's castle.

Sir Henry Stradling, whose body lies buried in the crypt under the chapel, was reputed to be a smuggler and known to indulge from time to time in a spot of piracy himself. Most of his contraband was brought from France and, during one of his many voyages, his ship was attacked by a Breton pirate, scuttled and left to sink with its cargo and crew aboard. Sir Henry was seized, held to ransom and became a bitter and resentful captive. He remained in the hands of the pirates for many months until the Stradling family paid a large sum of money for his release.

He never forgot the indignities he suffered during his captivity and for a long time sought to gain revenge. From a higher tower in his castle he kept a constant watch along the shore from St Athan to St Brides waiting for an opportunity to get even with the Bretons.

Finally, his vigil paid off when he saw a strange ship moored in the bay and a solitary raider standing on the shore. The sailor was seized, bound hand and foot and taken to Sir Henry. Soon the ship sailed off without the unfortunate captive. It may have been an ironic twist of fate, design or misfortune that marooned him at St Donat's but standing before Sir Henry was Peter, the Breton pirate who had captured him on the high sea and murdered his crew. Sir Henry's hatred was aroused and for revenge the prisoner was taken to the mouth of the Tresilian Cave beneath the castle walls. There he was made to watch a deep hole being dug and then he was buried alive in the sand until only his head and shoulders were uncovered.

No one can imagine the terror felt by the man as he listened to the waves crashing on the beach and watched the relentless tide sweep towards the cave entrance, knowing that, at any moment he would drown. Thousands of tides have come and gone since that fateful time, but to this day whenever a winter wind blows in from the sea, it is said the shrill cries of fright and despair are heard echoing through Tresilian Cave. In the light of the first full moon of a New Year, Peter can be heard crying aloud for help. It is said also that if he turns restlessly in his grave, then stormy weather is forecast.

Although the cave has sad connections, it also has its romantic tales too. According to old Welsh mythology it is believed to be one of the caves of Dwynwen, the Celtic Venus of love, and the home of an interesting legend concerning marriage and a archway.

It is said that if a person succeeded in throwing a stone across the arch or 'the bow of destiny', which is situated just below the roof of the cave, then he or she would be married within a year. If more than one stone had to be used, then he or she would be married more than once.

An old Welsh rhyme goes:

Where nymphs and swains resort to see
Fair Dwynwen's bow of destiny;
And, by athletic feat to know
Their near or distant marriage date,
Their path prescribed by line below
Their course inviolate.

It was in Tresilian cave that the parents of the celebrated General Sir Thomas Picton were married.

The story goes that Miss Cecil Powel, the heiress of Llandow was a very beautiful girl and had many admirers, both young and old. She was a high spirited girl, well ahead of her time, who wanted to enjoy life to its full and refused to tie herself to the bonds of marriage.

Most of her suitors were persistent, but she was usually successful in foiling their plans. One, Thomas Picton from Poyston in Pembrokeshire was more persistent than the rest and, although she liked him very much and wanted to marry him eventually, she felt that she was not ready for marriage yet. She decided to devise a scheme to cure him once and for all.

Cecil agreed to marry him on condition that the ceremony took place at the entrance to St Tresilian's cave. She then arranged for a fake ceremony to take place by bribing a local man to act as clergyman. Everyone present, including the 'parson' were to be masked. At the end of the service she would tell everyone to take off their masks and, when the parson was revealed as an imposter, she would announce that, because the marriage had not been performed by a man of the church, it must be annulled. Hopefully, the groom would be so upset at being the laughing stock of the community that he would leave her in peace until she was ready to accept his proposal.

Everything was arranged and Cecil arrived at the cave in a beautiful wedding dress accompanied by her bridesmaids. The ceremony took place and when over, the clergyman was asked to remove his mask. To her horror she discovered that the clergyman was none other than her father, the Reverend Edward Powel, Rector of Llandow. He and the groom had overheard her plotting and paid off the hired 'clergyman'.

Thankfully Cecil recovered from the shock and saw the funny side of the proceedings. She and her husband remained happily married, giving birth to a son, who later served his country as one of the Duke of Wellington's divisional commanders, before being killed at Quatre Bras.

The Stradling family remained at St Donat's for four centuries until Sir Thomas was killed in a duel in Paris on 27 September, 1738. It is also said that long ago another member of the family was murdered in the castle, and a ghostly figure of a stately old lady dressed in the clothes of long ago still appears from time to time. Wailing can be heard from behind the castle walls.

In 1925 the castle was purchased by William Randolph Hurst, the newspaper magnate, but ten years later, owing to financial difficulties he was forced to sell the castle. Today St Donat's is the home of Atlantic College, the first international sixth-form college in the world, accommodating more than 300 students from all parts of the world. Hardly a likely setting for a haunting. Yet even today when the castle stands fierce and black against the night sky and the wind moans through Tresilian Cave, many old folks will not pass by.

A Chariot for the Victors

Most people from Ystalyfera, a small village at the top end of the Swansea valley, know and proudly recall the story of the day the town band won the silver cup at the annual Cwmllynfell eisteddfod. But winning had not come easy.

It was always the same old story. With musical instruments tucked under their arms and heads bent, the members of the band would make their way back along the Cwmtwrch Valley. Every year their conductor, Morgan Rhys, would say the same words of encouragement with a crooked smile.

'Never mind, boys. Better luck next time.'

Then in the summer of 1850 their luck changed. On the day of the competition they made their way along the towpath to the Gurnos Basin, where the coal barges were turned on route from the colliery to the docks. There the path began its long slope up the valley, and beside them ran the black incline along which the trams ran to the colliery. As usual Morgan Rhys led the way, with the men following in silence one behind the other. Halfway up the mountain they stopped for a rest and, as they sat beside the path, Morgan rubbed his hands and said, 'mark my words, boys, this year we're going to win, I can feel it in my bones.'

By the time they arrived at Cwmllynfell crowds from villages all over the valleys had gathered already. All day the melodic strains of the bands could be heard in the hill side, filling the air with lyrical Welsh music. Finally it was the turn of the Ystalyfera town band. Morgan Rhys mounted the platform with an air of confidence and, facing the band, whispered 'Come on boys, give it all you got. The trophy is ours this year.'

They had chosen an arrangment of the old Welsh hymn *Bryn Calfaria*. Once they began to play the audience was left spellbound. Filled with renewed inspiration, the band was in complete harmony and even before the last note was played they knew the trophy was theirs.

Following the presentation they celebrated in true Welsh tradition with mead and ale flowing freely. Time and time again the silver cup was filled and passed around. Loosened by the ale the town band sang almost every song they knew. Eventually the evening drew to a close and it was time for the band to make their way home down through the valley. They started off laughing and joking but as the journey progressed they grew weary. Presently they came to the tramway sloping down to the Gurnos Basin and on which stood an empty tram at the top of the incline. Despite his tired bones Morgan mustered up all his strength and scrambled up the mound of slag, shouting to the boys as he went, 'Cerbyd i'r enillwyr!' 'A chariot for the victors!' All except the drummer, who couldn't manage the steep climb with his big base drum, quickly followed, laughing and shouting as they scrambled for a seat on the tram.

Overflowing with band members the tram began to trundle along the track, slowly at first but as it travelled further down the long incline it gathered speed rapidly with the men cheering. Suddenly they realised it was going too fast and, in desperation, Morgan pulled hard on the brake. A trail of sparks flew from the rails but the brake failed to slow the tram's progress and it continued to gather speed at an alarming rate. All the men could do was watch in horror as the end of the track grew nearer.

'Arglwydd mawr!' 'Great God!' they yelled. Several of the more agile members jumped over the side, their fall cushioned by the banks of coal dust. The rest of the band, trombones, tubas and cornets were plunged into the murky waters of Gurnos Basin.

Thankfully no one was seriously hurt in the collision, but for a number of years the silver cup they had so longed for and proudly won at Cwmllynfell lay buried beneath the muddy depths of the basin.

Tales of Garngoch Common
and Penlle'r-Gaer Woods

To the north-west of Swansea, there are many open spaces shrouded in mysteries and tales of long ago. For example, the stretch of wasteland, now known as Garngoch common, is thought to be an ancient burial ground. Garngoch, which means The Red Cairn or The Red Hill of a Sword, is said to have been named after a bloody battle fought there in the days of the Roman occupation, and the mound on the common is thought to contain the remains of those killed in battle. Garngoch is skirted by Penlle'r-gaer Woods — The Chief Place of The Legion — which is also of Roman origin. In an area with such an ancient history, it is hardly surprising to learn that there are many unexplained happenings relating to the common and woods.

One evening, a long time ago, a traveller riding south was crossing the common at Garngoch. As he passed Bryn Dafydd a sudden breeze swirled across the ground. It grew in strength until the ferns swayed and moaned. The traveller's horse hesitated, whined momentarily, then cantered across the common. In a short while the breeze settled, and everything was still again.

When the traveller came to the banks of the stream at Afon Llan, he dismounted and led the horse to the water's edge. He noticed the animal's hoofs were red with blood and immediately thought the animal had been injured. He carefully examined each leg and was astounded to find no wound. He walked the horse through the water and at once the blood stains were washed away. But the water flowed clear and, a few minutes later, the puzzled traveller returned to the saddle and went on his way.

Another tale tells of a tinker who was driving his horsedrawn cart along the path over the common. The lantern hanging from the cart swung from side to side making circles of light on the ground before him. All the while the pots and pans behind him clanged in rhythmic harmony as he went on his way. Suddenly they began to rattle louder, like the sounds of drums beating and swords clashing. For a moment it sounded as though some great battle was taking place and the tinker was terrified. Voices were heard crying out, some in great pain, others in anger. Stiff with fright the tinker sat and peered into the darkness but nothing stirred, except the ferns swaying in the wind. The ghostly battle raged for a while and then, just as suddenly, all was quiet. Eventually the frightened

tinker raised the whip to his horse and, with the lantern swinging wildly, hurried away.

Penlle'r-gaer Woods is not without its tales either. One day a grey damp mist clung to the trees when a young man came dashing out of the woods and through the lodge gates. There was fear in his eyes and he didn't stop running until he reached the local inn. With a few drinks inside him and, sitting besides a glowing fire, he began to tell his tale.

He had gone to the woods for a quiet stroll. Close behind him he heard the echo of footsteps and stopped, thinking it was someone he could walk with. There was no one on the path but the footsteps continued accompanied by a strange animal sound. At first he could not move with fear but then found superhuman strength and fled to safety. All the way to the inn he could hear someone or something close behind him but there were no footprints on the path and hoof marks had torn up the grass. All the way to the lodge he could hear snorting but once on the open road he could hear only his own footsteps and his heart beating wildly.

Another tale relates to an event which occurred more recently to a man who was travelling in the vicinity of Penlle'r-gaer from West Wales to Swansea along the A48 road. It was a dark night and rain was beating steadily on the windscreen. By mistake the man turned off the main road and found himself on an unfamiliar road. Desperately he peered out of the window in the hope of seeing a signpost to guide him. Shortly, in the car's headlights, he saw a solitary figure walking along the road. The driver stopped and asked the stranger, a young man, to direct him to the main Swansea road. He was extremely wet and his hair hung over his shoulders and an upturned collar hid his face. Without speaking a word, the stranger opened the car door and sat down on the passenger seat and pointed ahead. The driver followed his instructions and, after about a mile, passed a church and then the woods, all the while the stranger sitting silently alongside. All attempts at conversation failed and the driver wondered if he was dumb. When they reached a place called Cadle Mill the stranger indicated for the man to stop, got out of the car, smiled and walked into the darkness. The driver recognised the road and continued on his way, thankful for the silent man's assistance.

A few days later when returning to Carmarthen he reached the point where he had met the stranger. He found himself on an unfamiliar wide duel carriageway, and wondered if he was on the right road. Seeing a petrol station he stopped and made enquiries about the alternative route through Penlle'r-gaer Woods.

'Duw, where have you been these last few years?' exclaimed the pump attendant. 'There was a through road here once, but it has been closed for a while now. It went down by the church and past the woods.'

Ill at ease, the man thanked the attendant, and drove away as fast as the speed limit would allow.

Strange Encounters at Brandy Cove

The picturesque bay known today as Brandy Cove on the south coast of Gower, lies between Pwlldu head and Caswell. Once it was called Hareslade, but when it became a favourite haunt of smugglers its name was changed.

During the 19th century small boats could be seen bobbing among the breakers. The smugglers would steal ashore to disappear into the caves at the foot of the cliffs where they deposited their illicit goods. It was not only the seafaring men of the last century who haunted the cove. For more than forty years the ghostly voice of a woman, which was first heard late one afternoon in the autumn of 1920, tormented these caves.

When climbing the steep path leading from the beach a young couple were startled to hear a woman's screams echoing through the caves below. The couple looked towards the caves but saw nothing in the half light of dusk. Slowly they retraced their steps, approached the caves and stood for a while in silence listening for any sound. But they didn't hear the voice again, only the cries of the seagulls and decided they were mistaken and made for home.

Several days later a fishermen from the village of Murton

encountered a similar experience. He was walking along the water's edge when he heard a shrill cry from within the cave. He listened for a minute and then made his way up the cliff path. Again there was nothing to be seen and he dismissed the sounds as those of a sea bird.

In the years that followed this incident occurred time and time again. In the neighbouring villages of Pennard, Bishopston and Newton tales were told around many a fireside or public bar of the frightful screaming that came from deep within the cave. Although many spoke of the whistling wind or the distant cry of seagulls, none ventured near Brandy Cove after sunset. Finally, in November 1961 the mystery was solved.

The story goes that in 1919, there was much concern in Newton over the disappearance of an attractive young lady called Mamie Stuart. She had left her native Sunderland to begin a new life in South Wales. Before settling in the village she had lived for a while in Swansea with George Shotton, a marine engineer. He was later to appear before the Assizes charged with bigamously marrying her at South Shields Registry office in March 1915 and was sentenced to 18 months imprisonment.

Mamie was last seen on November 12, 1919 by the landlady of the Ship and Castle Inn. A thorough search of the house where she had lived revealed no trace of the missing woman, apart from a few clothes and personal belongings. George Shotton had, by now, been released from prison, but enquiries by the police which continued into the 1920's failed to find him. On 10 July the search was abandoned on the grounds that there was no evidence to support the theory that the missing woman was dead. So the mystery of Mamie Stuart was forgotten until 3 November 1961.

On this particular Sunday morning three young men from Bishopston went exploring in the caves of Brandy Cove. Their potholing expedition took them down an old lead mine air shaft, at the foot of which they passed through layers of rock which brought them into an anti-chamber. At the end of the chamber there was a tunnel which was blocked with boulders and probably led into the old mine workings. They moved the boulders and were confronted with what they thought was a wall. On closer investigation they found it was a three inch thick slab of stone, placed on end and resting against the boulders. Behind it they found the grisly remains of a human skeleton.

The police were called to the mine shaft but, because they were too large to enter the opening, the potholers had to recover the skeleton from its tomb.

Forensic examination revealed the body had lain there more than 20 years and was that of a woman aged about 25. Two rings found among the bones were later identified as being similar to those worn by Mamie Stuart. The coroner recorded a verdict of murder by person or persons unknown and concluded that the body had been concealed in the mine shaft shortly after her disappearance in 1919.

The bones were blessed and the remains buried in the churchyard at Bishopston where Mamie rests today. Since the winter of 1961 all has been quiet in the caves below the cliffs at Brandy Cove and locals will tell you that only the screams of the sea birds can be heard.

As for George Shotton, he was traced eventually to a cemetery in Bristol where his remains had been buried following his death in 1958, in his 78th year.

The Red Lady Who Was No Lady

The cave at Brandy Cove was not the only one to conceal a skeleton. Paviland, or Goat's Cave, is situated two miles south west of Rhosili and also hid a skeleton undiscovered for considerably longer than Mamie Stuart's.

A group of ardent geologists and naturalists comprising of John Trehorne, Matthew Moggridge, Gwyn Jeffreys, C. O. Francis, L.W. Dillwyn, and Miss Talbot had been searching the caves around the Gower Coast for several years. Since 1821 Dr William Buckland, first Professor of Geology at Oxford University, had been staying as a frequent guest of Miss Talbot at Penrice castle and often joined the party whenever his college duties allowed.

Two years later their efforts were rewarded and aroused much public interest when Buckland discovered part of a headless human skeleton in Paviland Cave. The bones had been stained red and around the neck was a necklace of wolf and reindeer teeth. As part of a burial ceremony it is believed the bones had been covered in red ochre to liven up the anaemic corpse. Buckland assumed that the skeleton was that of a priestess from the ancient Romano British period, and C.D. Morgan in his book '*Wanderings in Gower*', which was published in 1886, tells of a priestess from this period walking over the cliffs and living in the caves below. Because of these theories the skeleton became known as The Red Lady of Paviland, but everyone was surprised when, later on, it turned out that this was no lady at all.

In 1913 Professor Sallis of the Geology Department at Oxford decided to re-excavate the cave. With the help of more modern technology he discovered that the bones of the 'Red Lady' were in fact those of a slim young man of 25. More surprises were to follow when further examination indicated that the skeleton was a lot older than at first thought. This man had lived during the Palaeolithic period, the Old Stone Age, and was the earliest form of man as we know him today. He would have been more heavily built than today's man but he would have had the same anatomical characteristics and may have belonged to a group of hunters who lived in a rock shelter in the Dordogne region of France. Today the bones of this ancient man are kept in the basement of the Oxford University Museum.

Signs of a Passing Life

There are many stories in Wales about premonitions of death. Tradition recalls that St David was concerned at the way people were careless in their thoughts of the life to come. He prayed that they would be given certain signs of the immortality of the soul and of an eternal life to come, so that they could predict when death

comes and prepare themselves. Ever since that day these phantom deaths have been seen in many forms.

Some were in the form of a small light, called a corpse candle, and many believe these could only be seen in Glamorgan, although Tenby and St David's lay claim to a similar story. Others tell of carpenters hearing a coffin being assembled in their workshops at night, even before they had been asked to make one. There are other stories of strange knocking or footsteps fading into the distance in the home of a dying person. Stories of an apparition of a coffin resting, either in the home or on an object outside are also a frequent death sign in Glamorgan. In almost every village in Glamorgan there are innumerable references to phantom funeral processions which could be seen or heard leaving a home, moving slowly along a road or towards a church.

One such incident involved a farmer who had the misfortune to see his own funeral. One evening he was riding home from Cowbridge market when he saw a funeral procession winding down the lane leading from his farm to the main road. As the cortege approached he drew his horse to the side of the road to let the procession pass. To his horror he saw his wife, dressed in black following the coffin and supported by his eldest son. He watched the funeral disappear into the misty night and galloped home to be greeted by his wife and son who had heard him and came out to see what all the noise was. That night the farmer worried about what he had seen and within a few weeks he was taken ill whereupon he told his family about the happenings on that fateful night. Three days later he died.

It was not always the person concerned who would see his or her funeral. Sometimes it was the funeral of a near relative or a total stranger as this next story will show.

During the 19th century mounting stones, or up-blocks, were a common sight outside many public places such as taverns or churches. These consisted of a set of steps, about two feet high, to help travellers to get into their coaches or mount their horses.

A few miles beyond Bridgend is the village of Bryncethin where outside the Mason Arms, you will find a set of mounting stones exactly as they would have stood over a hundred years ago when this story took place.

One day at dusk, the innkeeper's young daughter sat looking out of the window at the carpet of snow glistening on the ground and hugging the rooftops. After a while, in the dimming light, she saw one of the strangest sights she had ever seen and called her father.

'Look dada, look,' she cried pointing to the forecourt of the tavern. She looked in amazement at a coffin resting on the mounting stones for, although it was quite real to her, there was no one to be seen only a trail of footprints in the snow leading to and from the tavern door. Her father looked through the window only to see a pristine covering of snow on the empty courtyard and a drift of snow heaped against the steps. The coffin and footsteps had suddenly and mysteriously disappeared as they had appeared. Because this was the age of superstitions and the villagers were obsessed about such matters, neither the innkeeper nor his daughter told anyone about the strange incident.

A few weeks later a farmer from further down the valley died. On the day of the funeral at Llansantffraid church a heavy fall of snow covered the ground and, by the time the cortege reached the Mason's Arms on its way to Bryncethin, all were exhausted and they decided to rest. The exact coffin the girl had seen in her vision was placed on the mounting stones, and the bearers and mourners went in to the tavern to warm themselves by the blazing log fire, leaving their footprints in the snow. After a few tots of whisky to stave off the biting cold they set off on their journey to the churchyard.

Witches and Wizards

By 1893, it was said, all the witches in Glamorgan were dead and buried. Whether true or not we may never know, but there are enough tales remaining to fill a book. It is believed that, in exchange for certain powers, witches had made an agreement with the Devil to abandon Christianity and follow him. One such witch was the Witch of Wenvoe.

A long time ago a young man had promised to marry a girl from Cadoxton but, unfortunately for him the girl was a niece of the Witch of Wenvoe. When the young man jilted her for a prettier girl, the witch was so outraged she vowed to take revenge on him. She was so furious she untwisted the girdle from around her waist and placed it on the threshold of the house where the newly wedded couple were to live. Everyone gathered at the house to welcome the new couple but as the bride and groom stepped over the girdle the groom was immediately transformed into a werewolf. Broken hearted he ran off towards Bear's Wood. Every night he could be heard howling outside the Witch of Wenvoe's house and terrifying everyone in the village. His unlucky bride became ill with worry and was ostracised by the locals. Within a year of their marriage she had died of a broken heart.

When the Witch heard this she was delighted, and decided to turn the werewolf back into a man so that at last he would marry her niece. She did this by throwing a charmed lambskin over him immediately changing him into human form. Now relieved to be a normal person again, the man agreed to marry the niece. However, he treated his second wife so badly that the witch was forced to place a curse on him again. Unfortunately for him the Witch died suddenly so, because no power on earth could restore him to the human race, the poor man was condemned to be a werewolf for the rest of his life. He became known as 'the wildman of the woods' and roamed the area as a werewolf until he was killed by a stray shot from a poacher's gun.

Glamorgan witches also had the ability to transform themselves into geese. One who lived near Porthcawl often could be seen flying over the sand dunes between Margam and Porthcawl. She was the wife of an innkeeper who was very fond of cheating and overcharging her customers. One day she overcharged the local witch who immediately turned her into a wild goose. For over a year she flew over the same sand dunes as the witches until one day she quarrelled with the other geese and, in a fight, lost a piece of ribbon tied to her wing as a distinguishing mark. Once the ribbon was lost the witches spell was broken and she returned once more to human life.

Although there are many stories of witches and fairies in the Glamorganshire area, tales of wizards seem to be rather thin on the ground.

Twm Ifan Prys of Penfrydd, near Pontrhydyfen was a wizard who lived in the 16th century. He was a descendant of a prominent local poet and became, as a young child, he was making predictions he became known as Twm Celwydd Teg - Tom of the White Lies. However, these predictions, whether good or bad, always proved right and, as his fame spread, his popularity with the ruling classes diminished.

One day Twm foretold that the son of Sir George Herbert, a local lord, would hang himself by the string of his own garment. For making such an outrageous prediction Twm was thrown into Kenfig Castle. But when later the child was found dead in his cradle, having twisted around and suffocated by his own pinafore strings, Twm was released and given a sum of money. From then on Twm decided not to make his talents known and took casual farm work, mainly as a thresher of corn.

The locals, however, never forgot his talents and would consult him about such things as the weather or yield of crops. On one occasion a young boy asked Twm what the future held for him. Twm looked at him sadly, and shook his head grimly. 'Before the night is out my boy, you will die three times'. The boy laughed at such an outrageous statement, thinking how could anyone die three times. Later that day seeing a small tree standing next to the river the youth decided to climb up and steal some eggs from a kite's nest. As he put his hand into the nest an adder, which had been brought home by the kite to feed her young, bit him. He lost his footing, fell and broke his back on a protruding branch before plummeting into the river below and drowning. Thus the sorcerer's prediction of dying three times that night was fulfilled.

The Verry Volks of Gower

The legendary Gower fairies are known locally as the Verry Volks. There are many tales told of these little people, who were about the size of children and usually dressed in red or green.

One story concerns the tenant of Eynon's Ford Farm, near the village of Reynoldston. It was originally a typical long-house occupied by both family and cattle. The dwelling area comprised of two living rooms on the ground floor and two bedrooms above. The other part of the building was the cow-house and stable. A common entrance led into a passage which was used by both man and beast and was wide enough to admit the long horned cattle. Today, a quarter of a mile down a path leading south in the direction of Penrice Woods, you will find a much modernised farm bearing the name it was given over 200 years ago.

Our tale begins one summer's night long ago when the farmer was woken to the sound of strange music coming from the cattle stalls. He was puzzled but when he realised where the music was coming from he made his way to the passageway that divided the dwelling house from the animal stalls. There he was amazed to see the building teeming with little people, the Verry Volks, all dressed in scarlet and green. Some were dancing on the back of his favourite ox, others reeled around the pebbled floor, whilst others played fiddles and pipes. Rivetted to the floor the farmer stood and watched as the merrymaking continued. Finally the music stopped and the ox was led into the middle of the stable and fed a mixture of mysterious herbs. Suddenly the farmer realised they had killed the ox and were expertly stripping the hide from its back. They proceeded to cut the meat into thousands of little pieces, laying the bones carefully in a pile on the floor as they worked. Another group were preparing a fire and began roasting the meat over the flames. The feasting and dancing went on for several hours. Although the farmer was distressed at what he saw, he could not move and even if he could he was afraid to offend them because no one upset the Verry Volks.

Finally the laughter and music began to fade and the Verry

Volks collected the bones and began to reassemble the carcass on the floor. Piece by piece, like some complicated metal puzzle the beast began to take shape. In no time at all the skeleton stood life-like in the middle of the fairy circle. Next they carefully lifted the hide from the beams and began draping it like a shroud over the skeleton, and smoothed it down. As one of the fairies began to smooth the hide over one foreleg she noticed a tiny bone was missing. Everyone shrieked at one another and became angry. For several hours they looked high and low but the bone was nowhere to be found. Eventually exhausted they gave up and the farmer returned to his bed, thinking he would never see his ox alive again.

The following morning he went to the stall and was amazed to see his favourite animal with its head bent over the feeding trough munching at the hay. Dismissing the whole incident as a strange dream the farmer led the ox out to pasture only to notice it was slightly lame in the foreleg. From then until the day it died, the old ox always walked with a limp

Another tale concerning the Verry Volks dates from around 1799 and is reputed to be the last place visited by the fairies. One day a wizen old lady knocked on the door of Lagadranta farmhouse, near Broughton Bay, Llanmadoc and asked the farmer's wife if she could borrow a sieve. The farmer's wife told her she didn't have one but the old woman enquired about the one over the vat straining hops which the wife had forgotten about. Immediately, suspecting the caller to be one of the 'verry volk' who were renown in the area for sifting gold, the farmer's wife gave her the sieve she was using.

A few days later the old lady returned the sieve saying, 'since you were good enough to lend me the sieve, the largest cask in the farmhouse will contain the most potent beer you have ever brewed and will never be without beer'. The farmer's wife was told not to tell anyone about the cask and, after she had agreed to do so, the old lady turned away from the door and disappeared into a well at the bottom of the garden. The farmer's wife was delighted and soon the increased potency of her beer became the talk of the village, thanks to the fairies.

During harvest time the local taverns were deserted as farmers from Cheriton and Llangennydd came by horse and cart to sample the special brew at Lagadranta, which means 'eye of the stream'. Night after night the jugs were filled and refilled, but however much was used the cask remained full.

One day the farmer's wife could keep the secret no longer and began bragging to the neighbours how she had lent the fairies her hop straining sieve and in exchange had been blessed with a special brew. That night the spell was broken and the cask ran dry, never to fill again. From that day, I suspect the farmer's wife was no longer popular with the men of the village.

The Ruler Who Liked War

One of the many mysteries of the Gower Peninsula is Pennard Castle. Although no records exist, it is thought to have been built in the 13th century. In Edmund Vale's book entitled '*The World of Wales*', he lists 76 castles, and mentions Pennard as, 'A ruin about which nothing appears to be known'. However, the local folk will tell you differently.

They say the castle was built overnight on a Viking stronghold by a Welsh sorcerer to save himself from the invading Normans. But surely a man capable of building a castle overnight could have fought off a few war-mongering Normans?

Another story tells of a well known chief who lived at the castle and was fond of fighting. He had gathered together a band of men who were as blood thirsty as himself and their fame had spread throughout Dyfed and Powys. In fact he would help any Welsh ruler who needed assistance in battle.

One day he received a message that a king in Gwynedd had been threatened by a neighbouring prince whose army was twice as strong as his own. Within an hour the Gower warriors were riding northwards, swords at the ready.

After winning the battle for the king, the Gower chief was offered a reward and, instead of accepting the usual gold or silver, he asked for the hand of the King's daughter in marriage. The King could not refuse because the chieftain had twice saved his life. At first the daughter was alarmed because she knew about the chief's violent reputation. She had a gentle nature and could not see the forced marriage working. She was a lover of flowers and birds not war and, it was said, a favourite with the fairies. Soon, however, she realised that the chieftain loved her very much, and had no intention of making her unhappy.

Elated at winning the battle and a wife, he returned to Pennard and threw a great feast, calling to his servants to prepare, 'mountains of meat and seas of ale'. Soon the merriment was in full swing. The soldiers began singing and dancing and it wasn't long before they became very drunk.

A sentry, on guard on the castle wall, heard strange sounds and looked into the valley below. At first he must have thought he had drunk too much ale, for there on the grass he saw a flickering circle of light. Puzzled he stumbled down to the warden who, in a drunken stupor, was slumped in a corner chair by the fire. Finally he managed to rouse him and together they watched as the flickering green patch danced before their eyes. Still puzzled, they ran to the hall and called the chief, who, thinking it was an excuse for yet another battle, gave the order, 'To arms'. Fighting drunk, they staggered down the slope of the castle and approached the grassy area. In the moonlight, they saw a group of fairies singing and dancing in celebration for the king's daughter. The warriors burst into the ring brandishing their swords, but of course the fairies could only be seen and not touched. Suddenly a voice rang out: 'Unfortunate chief! Thou hast warrest against those who shall destroy thee. Thou hast wantonly spoiled our innocent sport and for that thy castle and township shall be destroyed'.

Suddenly it became cold and the fairies vanished. Clouds of sand swirled up the valley from the sea, filling the warriors' eyes, ears and mouths until their lifeless bodies littered the area. The force of the gale sent the sand billowing over the houses and castle and, within a few hours, everything was completely buried. Where the storm came from we do not know but it has been said that on that same evening a mountain of sand mysteriously disappeared from Ireland.

Like every good castle, Pennard has its ghost too, the Gwarch-y-rhibyn. The apparition takes the form of the Irish banshee, a night hag. She has long black hair, sunken eyes, a crooked back, a thin figure, and flapping wings and is seen wearing a long black flowing robe. It is thought to be unlucky to sleep in the castle and apparently one man who did was found unconscious with bruises on his body and deep facial cuts. When he woke the following morning he described the hag who 'clawed like an eagle and pecked at his body'. Shortly after this incident he went insane and eventually died in an asylum.

The Devil Visits Glamorgan

It seems that the devil was a frequent visitor to this corner of Wales. It is not always clear whether the devil was thought to be the Evil One of Christian teaching or simply an inferior demon. In the following tales, I shall leave you to draw your own conclusions.

The old Inn called The Dusty Forge, on the main Cowbridge to Cardiff road, was built on the site of an old smithy. Legend tells that one day at midnight the blacksmith's wife heard a noise coming from the forge and went to investigate. There she found the devil hammering out on the anvil a shoe for his own cloven foot. The woman rushed to the chicken house and woke the cock. Thinking it was dawn the cock began to crow and the devil, who feared sunlight, dropped the half finished shoe and disappeared.

Two stories relate to events which happened at Crack Hill. As you travel from Bridgend along the main Cardiff road, you will pass over the Ewenny Bridge and through the litte hamlet of Brocastle. Eventually you reach Crack Hill, an old Roman road which, during the 18th century, was edged with a dry-stone wall. Near the bottom of the hill stood a milestone indicating it to be five miles to Cowbridge.

Crack Hill was a eerie desolate place and superstitious locals

believed it to be a favourite haunt of the devil. During the 19th century this was confirmed by two travellers who swore under oath that they had encountered the devil.

One traveller who lived at Pentre Meyrick was making his way home from Bridgend. Black ominous clouds loomed above and the occasional rumble of thunder could be heard in the distance. The traveller dug his heels into the horse's flank and it broke into a gentle trot. As they reached the lower slope of Crack Hill the traveller heard the clip-clop of the horse's hoofs, then, faintly at first, he heard the sound of another horse approaching. He turned in the saddle but the road was deserted. Again he heard the sound and, although he saw nothing, felt a rider pass close by and continue galloping up the hill.

Back and fore along Crack Hill the galloping hoofs were quite audible but still there was neither horse or rider to be seen. Once, as the rider passed by, the traveller felt something clutching at his shoulders, as though someone had leapt onto his back. His horse shied, throwing him to the ground, and, as it ran off up the hill, the traveller scrambled to his feet with something still clinging to his shoulders. Terrified he swung round several times in an attempt to free himself from the burden, but whatever it was would not let go. Finally he clambered up Crack Hill, struggling against the weight and crying out to God in fright. As he neared the top of Crack Hill a bolt of lightening lit up the road and, as suddenly as the burden had come upon him, it released itself and he was free once more. For the last time he heard the galloping hoofs as the phantom steed returned for its rider. After a moment or two there was silence and the traveller continued his journey in peace.

The second incident concerns another lone traveller making his way from Bridgend to Cowbridge, this time on foot. He reached the bottom of Crack Hill and began to walk up the steep incline but soon found himself slowing down. Thinking he was tired he struggled on but it became increasingly difficult for him to keep up a normal walking pace. Half way up he felt as though he was carrying a heavy load and, glancing sideways, felt something or someone clinging to his shoulders. Panic stricken, he began to run but found the weight too much. He tried to shake off the burden but failed and had to grit his teeth and struggle on. As he neared the top of the hill he cried out in despair and the weight suddenly left his shoulders. Before his eyes he watched as a black and red bundle rolled down the hill into a disused quarry and exploded in a shower of sparks and smoke. The air was filled with the smell of sulphur and, as you can imagine, the man reached his destination in record time. For many years after locals would not travel up Crack Hill at night.

One of the oldest and most amusing tales I have come across concerning the work of the devil is set on the northern boundaries of Swansea. Just off the M4 motorway lies the tiny village of Llangyfelach nesting on a hill-side looking northwards to the moors of Mynydd y Gwair. It was once renown for its hiring fairs but according to legend these fairs fell into disrepute because the prospective mistress was 'too often mistaken for the maid'.

Llangyfelach holds the unique distinction of having the only church in the County of Glamorgan with a detached tower. Of course, with anything unusual in Wales, there is usually an interesting legend attached to it, and the lone tower at Llangyfelach Church is no exception.

The story goes that one day the Devil was watching St Cyfelach building his church and became so envious of the impressive building that he decided to make off with the tower for himself. St Cyfelach immediately cursed and swore at the Devil who became frightened and dropped the tower less than 100 yards away from where he had picked it up.

The tower remains today but the old church was demolished for structural reasons to be replaced by one built on a safer site slightly to the north. It is well proportioned and worth a visit and, besides the old tower, the church contains some interesting and unusual artifacts.

The Queen of Song

Up the Valley from Swansea stands Craig-y-Nos castle. It was once the home of Adelina Patti, the famous opera singer who became known throughout Europe as the Queen of Song. Madam Patti bought the castle in 1878 and restored it to please her Italian husband, Ernesto Nicolini. It was the first domestic home in the area to have electricity installed. Prior to this she lived in Waterson Court on the outskirts of Bridgend.

Legends say that long before Adelina went to live at Craig-y-Nos, which means Rock of the Night, fairies kept a hoard of gold in a cave underneath it. To get into the castle they climbed the wall using a ladder made of twenty pure gold rungs. Once inside the courtyard they would make for the cave, the entrance to which was topped by a huge stone.

Madam Patti was born in Madrid and brought up in New York and, although not Welsh, she loved Wales and the friendliness of the people. Even though she was a celebrated singer who travelled the world, she never forgot her love for the people of Glamorgan.

There is a tale still told in the area concerning her fondness for Kitty, a widow who kept the Miller's Arms, near where the rivers Garw and the Ogmore meet.

One summer, long before Adelina moved in to Craig-y-Nos Castle, she and her husband came to the area for the salmon fishing season. They stayed in the village of Brynmenyn — hill of butter — so called because of the carpet of golden gorse that grew there. Each evening they would rest at the Inn and talk to Kitty and the locals. Adelina would tell them tales of lands far beyond Wales while Kitty would talk of her homeland and the hills and beauty of Glamorgan. Adelina and her husband came often to the Miller's Arms and, as the years went by, a strong friendship grew.

One evening as Kitty was standing at the door waving goodbye to Madam Patti, a traveller who had stopped at the Inn recognised Adelina and asked another customer what the two women had in common. Kitty was shocked to overhear the traveller refer to her friend as 'Baroness Patti, the famous opera singer'. Although the two women became good friends and Kitty never tired of the tales of cites in Europe, Adelina's homeland of Madrid and America, she never asked Adelina about herself, and was unaware of the singer's great fame.

The next time they met, Kitty was unusually quiet. There was no fun or laughter in the old widow's voice, and Adelina was puzzled wondering if her friend was sick or if she had offended her in some way. When she asked the regulars what was wrong they told her the reason for Kitty's awkwardness. Taking Kitty's hands in hers, she said with compassion, 'My voice is a gift that I must share with the world, especially my closest and dearest friends'. That night, the voice that had thrilled kings and princes throughout Europe, sang in that little Inn in Wales for her dearest friend. The song Adelina choose was so fitting to the occasion and it brought tears to Kitty's eyes:

'Mid pleasures and palaces
   Though we may roam,
 Be it ever so humble,
 There's no place like home.

Many years after this incident Madam Patti went to live in Craig-y-Nos Castle and the song she sang at the Miller's Arms became one of her favourites. It was a special request at many of her concerts and, it is said, every time she sang it she would think of Kitty, the Miller's Arms and the yellow carpeted hills and salmon jumping in the rivers around Brynmenyn village.

The people of Glamorgan were very fond of their famous 'adopted' daughter, and in 1912 she was made a 'Freeman' of the then town of Swansea, an honour which in 1897 the people of Brecon had bestowed on her. The baroness presented the Winter Gardens, which had been erected in Craig-y-Nos and used as a walking area on rainy days, to the town Council of Swansea. It became known as the Patti Pavilion and today can be seen in Victoria Park, a short distance from the bay. To the people of Glamorgan, Adelina Patti will always be remembered as 'their' Queen of Song.

The Saint Saved By The Seagulls

In the days of the reign of King Arthur, there lived a noble Prince of Brittany called Dihocus. He had a very beautiful daughter and he became obsessed by her, fell madly in love and seduced her. She became pregant and gave birth to St Cenydd, Gower's own Saint. When the child was born the calf of the child's leg was firmly attached to his thigh — some say as a punishment for the father's sin. There are many interesting tales about St Cenydd, but the most interesting surrounds his birth.

King Arthur, who ruled Britain at the time, was holding court at nearby Loughor on Christmas Day and Dihocus and his daughter were invited. Although heavily pregnant, she decided to go, and gave birth to the boy among the tents. The prince, fearing a scandal, ordered the child to be placed in a moses like basket and cast into the river to drift down the Burry Estuary and out to sea. These were cruel times too and since every man either had to work or fight, weaklings were considered a burden on the rest of the community, and, like in the animal kingdom were often left to die.

Suddenly a terrible storm blew up and lashed the west coast of Wales, but the cradle remained upright and safe. As the wind and rain drove the cradle over the waves, seagulls encircled it. They held it firmly in their beaks and gently guided it to the safe haven of Worm's Head to rest in a hollow on the rocks. Some of the birds set to work making a bed of feathers, whilst others protected the child from the biting wind with their wings.

An angel of God placed a little brass bell by the child's head and the story goes that whenever he was hungry an obliging doe filled it with milk. Ever since the bell has been affectionately referred to as 'The Titty Bell' or '*Cloch Tethan*', from the Latin *cloch* meaning bell and *teth* meaning teat.

The nourishment from the bell was sweeter than honeycomb and so pure that normal bodily functions did not occur. Also it is reputed that the clothes the child was wrapped in grew with him and never decayed.

For 18 years St Cenydd remained on Worm's Head, taught by an angel, until God instructed him to move about a mile away to Burry Holmes where he built a hermitage. He was said to be a gentle man who radiated happiness around him and consequently his fame spread throughout Gower and beyond. He carried his 'Titty Bell' with him and it is reputed that one touch enabled him to skim the water to St David, his friend in Pembrokeshire. On another occasion it was used to 'cure' his leg so that he could attend a religious gathering. It is also claimed that a flock of seagulls were St Cenydd's constant companions. When he died he was carried by his own disciples to be buried in his monastery. A crowd of seagulls joined them and toned down their cries to blend in with the chanting of the monks.

How true these legends are no one can tell, but from documentary evidence it appears that there was a religious settlement at Burry Holmes. Furthermore, it is reported that in 986 A.D. the Danes burnt down a priory on the site where Llangenydd Church now stands.

The church is full of evidence of St Cenydd's existence. The lynch-gate, the only one in Gower, was presented to the church in 1903. It is beautifully carved and depicts some of the incidents in the life of St Cenydd, as related in Capgrave's book, 'Nova Legends Angliae', which was printed in Latin and published in 1526.

Inside the church, in the centre of the west wall, is a stone base of a Celtic Cross, elaborately carved with an interfacing design. This is believed to be the coffin lid of St Cenydd's tomb and since time immemorial locals have referred it as St Cenydd's Stone. It is recorded also that his skull, reputed still to be in existence in the 15th century, was used by the people of Llangenydd for swearing formal oaths.

Another interesting relic that could have been conncected with St Cenydd was discovered in the hamlet of Cwm Ivy. In a field, Parc-yr-Odyn or The Field of the Kiln, a local farmer ploughed up a curious rectangular shape bell thought to have been made from gold. Some say it is an ancient bell used by the Irish Saints or could this have been the Titty Bell of St Cenydd? Sadly it has disappeared and we are unable to use modern techniques to establish its age.

Until the early 1900's the people of Llangenydd always remembered St Cenydd on 5 July — St Cenydd's Day. It was a time for celebration and people from all corners of Gower would gather to join in the dancing, cock-fighting and many other highlights. There would be stalls serving various sweetmeats, but the most interesting was a traditional Llangenydd dish called 'whitepot'. This was made from flour, milk and currants, blended together and baked in a hot oven to commemorate the milk that flowed from St Cenydd's titty bell.

A pole would be attached to Llangenydd Church tower and a wooden cock, covered in white calico, draped in red and blue ribbons would be raised. This represented the seagulls who looked after St Cenydd and became his life-long companions.

The Mabsant or Saint's Day was a remnant from early Celtic times. Although the origin was probably pagan, it was taken over and modified by the Christian Church. By the 16th century, the religious meaning had disappeared but they continued as an excuse for a rowdy celebration. Sadly such interesting traditions have been forgotten.

The Fairies Revenge At Pantannas

Unlike the fairies who frequented the Gower Peninsula, those who haunted other parts of Glamorgan were called the Bendith y Mamau, the Mothers' Blessing, and it appears they weren't quite so good natured.

Once there was a farmer at Pantannas, near Quaker Yard, in the parish of Merthyr Tydfil who disliked the fairies who paid frequent visits to his fields. 'A noisy boisterous tribe', he would call them. This was most upsetting to the fairies because he had several fields where they preferred to dance.

One day a witch told the farmer if he ploughed the grassland where the fairies enjoyed congregating and planted wheat he would rid himself of them forever. This he did immediately. The fairies stopped coming and so did the sound of their music that kept him awake night after night. The farmer was delighted until one day, when returning home, he saw a small man in a red coat brandishing a little sword. Pointing at the farmer he said menacingly:

'Vengeance is coming. It is approaching soon.'

Although the farmer laughed, there was something about this little man's sternness that made him feel uneasy. A few nights later a voice repeated the warning to him. Then one night during harvest time, the whole corn crop was burnt and the barn too. The following day the farmer met the little man in the red coat again.

'It's only beginning,' the fairy said in a menacing voice.

The farmer, now scared, tried to pacify the fairy by promising to restore the meadows, but the fairy said that the word of the fairy king had been given and vengeance would take place, whatever happened. The farmer was deeply distressed at losing his harvest, and finally, after much pleading, the fairy said he would speak to his master and meet him again on the third day at the hour of sunset When the farmer arrived, the little man was already sitting by the side of the road. He said the king had relented and said revenge would not take place in his lifetime nor that of his children. A century passed and the family were beginning to get used to the occasional voice threatening revenge, but weren't unduly worried. In fact it became a family joke.

Then one Christmas the heir to Pantannas, a man called Rhydderch, was celebrating his engagement to Gwerfyl, the daughter of a neighbouring farmer. The party was in full swing, a goose was roasting over a spilt, when they heard a piercing voice thundering through the air. It shrieked its evil warning from the Black Cauldron of the river Taff, 'The time for vengeance has come'.

That night the heir walked with his fiancee to her home at Pen Craig Daf Farm but never returned. His parents hunted the countryside for him but found no trace. Finally, because of the warning, it was assumed he had been lured into a fairy ring or taken to one of their caves in Darren-y-Cigfrain — The Raven's Rift. In desperation his mother consulted a wise man, who could give her little comfort. That night an old lady appeared to the mother and said that she would never see her son again because the long threatened revenge finally had taken place. She did, however, say there may be a faint possibility that her son would reappear in the distant future, but certainly not in her lifetime.

Soon the fiancee died of a broken heart and then, after many years, the parents died. All the while there was no sign of the fairies.

What no one knew was that Rhydderch had been taken to the fairy cave. Many years later, one summer afternoon he asked if he could return to his family. Permission was granted and he raced over the hills, thinking that he had only been in the cave for a few days. Rhydderch immediately went to Pen Craig Daf Farm to look for his intended bride, but all were strangers to him, and the farm looked different, older, he thought. He asked about Gwerfyl, but no one had heard of her. Rhydderch sank into a chair in disbelief. Surely someone, somewhere knew his bride. The puzzled farmer recalled a story that had been told to him by his grandfather about a youth who had disappeared some hundreds of years ago. As the farmer got up from his chair he accidentally knocked his walking stick against Rhydderch's foot and he immediately vanished into a shower of dust. Some say that if you pass the area in the dead of night you will hear a haunting voice whispering, 'Vengeance is over'.

The Devil of Bryn-y-Wrach

Old Morgan sold bibles throughout South Glamorgan. He tramped from Brynmenyn up the Ogmore Valley to Aberkenfig, then north-east along the road to call at each village until he reached Lewistown. From there he would take the winding path over Bryn-y-Wrach to Llangeinor before making his way back to Brynmenyn through the Garw Valley. He was a familiar sight wearing a three quarter coat, a brimmed hat and carrying a satchel filled with black bound bibles. Along the route he also frequented many of the taverns where he would stop for a mug of ale or a night's rest.

One day, as he was climbing the slopes of Bryn-y-Wrach, the sky became overcast and an icy wind blew down the mountain path. Having travelled all day, he was tired and his satchel weighed heavily on his shoulders. Then he saw the grey walls of Ael-y-bryn, a little hillside farm where his old friend Elias John lived. He knew there would be a blazing fire and a warm comfortable bed inside for him so he battled through the biting wind. When he reached the farm he knocked on the door with his knobbly stick. After several minutes it was opened by Elias's daughter Mair, a hard hearted girl, who looked at Morgan coldly.

'Good evening,' he said politely. 'Tell your father that his old friend Morgan has called on his way to Llangeinor.'

'He's out', Mair snapped and slammed the door in his face.

Darkness was closing in and the wind sliced through his old worn clothes. He knew he wasn't strong enough to continue over the mountain and, because he knew Elias would make him welcome, he decided to shelter in the barn and wait for his friend's return.

After resting for a while on the straw floor he saw bright lights in the farmhouse and thought he heard laughter coming from the kitchen. Curious at the merriment, he crept over to the window and was surprised to see Meredith sitting at the table. He was a farm hand who, the previous year, had been caught flirting with Mair. Elias, armed with a pitchfork, had chased him from the farm and had forbidden him to see his daughter.

For a while Morgan watched as Mair brought a steaming meat pie from the oven and placed it on the table. This was followed by two flagons of ale from the larder. As the couple were about to eat their meal, they heard horses's hoofs on the cobbled courtyard. Mair became agitated, hid the pie beneath the pendulum of the grandfather clock, hurriedly pushed the flagons into a butter churn and helped Meredith into the spacious boiler that stood in the corner of the kitchen.

As Elias approached, Morgan stepped from the shadows of the house and greeted his friend.

'Elias my friend, how are you?'

The two men embraced each other.

'Morgan, my old pal, do come in.'

Elias unlatched the door and led him into the kitchen.

'Warm yourself by the fire Morgan. You must stay the night, it is biting cold out there. Mair a hot drink and a bite to eat for our guest.'

Morgan sat with his feet on the hearth and Mair scowled at him.

'There's only cheese and a stale piece of the bread in the larder,' she snapped.

Together the two men sat talking over old times, as they nibbled on the cheese. From the corner of his eye Morgan could see Mair's eyes darting towards the boiler in the corner of the room.

After an hour Elias threw more logs onto the fire and they chatted about Old Nell, the Knowing One, who Morgan claimed had shown him the secret of her mysterious spells. Elias's eyes lit up with interest and he pulled his chair closer. A mischievous smile wrinkled Morgan's face as he told Elias he knew why the woman never starved even though she was all alone in her mountain hut and found it difficult to go out to buy food.

'Look, I'll show you', said Morgan excitedly. He raised his hands, and in a solemn voice began to chant. 'Hear me, Spirit of the mountains.'

Then he took a handful of salt from the table and sprinkled it onto the fire. As the blue flames rose, he told Elias that the spell was cast and he would produce a tasty supper for them both. Morgan rose from his chair, went over to the grandfather clock and brought out the still warm pie. Then, removing the lid on the butter churn, he lifted out the two flagons of ale and placed them on the table.

Elias was astounded, but Mair was dismayed as she watched the two men devour her lover's supper. They enjoyed their meal and, after a few more tales, Morgan announced that he had the power to summon Satan himself.

'Arglwydd mawr, Great God!' exclaimed Elias as he crossed himself.

'He doesn't usually show himself to good Christian folk, but I will summon him so that if he does try to set his foot on the slopes of Bryn-y-Wrach you will know who you must drive from your doorstep.'

Once more Morgan raised his arms and began chanting. This time he walked over to the boiler and lit the wood under the boiler. Mair stifled a cry of horror and ran from the room.

'Here, take my stick', announced Morgan, 'and if the devil appears you must fill his black heart with terror, and banish him from this place forever.'

Minutes passed as the two men sat looking at the flames licking the sides of the boiler.

'He knows he will find no welcome here' said Elias as he watched the boiler, stick poised ready to hit out.

Suddenly the blue flames rose higher and a sound, like the roar of thunder, was heard from within the boiler. A moment later the lid flew off, crashed to the floor, and the shadowy figure of Meredith leapt from the boiler as though he had just escaped from the furnace of Hell. Through the smoke Elias rushed towards him and with an oath began beating him on the head and shoulders. Meredith dashed for the door with Elias in hot pursuit and escaped into the darkness.

'Great God,' Elias gasped at last. 'I would never have thought . . . ', then he gave a little chuckle.

'You know Morgan, my old boy, as the devil dashed through the door, I thought he had the face of that farm hand I chased from the farm last summer.'

That night Morgan, wrapped in a blanket, slept peacefully in the cupboard bed beside a blazing fire. As for Mair I expect she spent the night sobbing and thinking of the way she had spoken to Morgan earlier that night.

The Women of Mumbles Head

With so much rugged coastline in Glamorganshire it is hardly surprising to hear of many heroic rescues taking place. One of the most famous stories must be the dramatic tale of Jessie and Margaret Ace, who became known as the Grace Darlings of Wales. Their father was Abraham Ace, the lighthouse keeper at Mumbles Head.

On a blistery night in January 1883, a fierce storm engulfed the Bristol Channel. The Prussian vessel, Admiral Prinz Adelbert of Danzig, lost her rudder and was being towed by the steam-tug, Flying Scud. The rope snapped and the barque crashed onto the rocks about a quarter of a mile west of Mumbles Head. As the storm bell sounded the Mumbles lifeboat, 'Wolverhampton', was launched with her crew of seven and six volunteers. They battled against the elements and, when they drew alongside the vessel, they rescued two men. As they were hauling a third man to safety a sudden surge of sea swept the mast from the Admiral Prinz Adelbert and the lifeboat crashed against the wreck throwing some of the crew into the sea. Others hung on to lifelines whilst several swam to the shelter of nearby caves.

For a while Coxswain Jenkins, despite head injuries, clung to the upturned lifeboat, searching for his four sons who were members of the crew. He was able to pull one out of the water and scrambled ashore with him on the crest of the next breaker. Sadly, his son was already dead and, exhausted, all he could do was call for assistance.

His cries were heard by the lighthouse keeper, the keepers two daughters and a soldier, Gunner Edward Hutchings. They raced to the water's edge where two other crewmen were being driven onto the rocks. Ignoring their father's warning, the women waded out into the icy water. Knotting their shawls together they threw them to the drowning men and, together with the two men, hauled them to safety.

The story hit the headlines and, like all good tales, it was immortalised in a ballad entitled 'The Women of Mumbles Head'. It was written by the famous Victorian writer, Clement Scott, and

was a popular act in the music halls of the day. Although it isn't actually correct and much of the narrative has been contradicted in official accounts, it touched the hearts of the nation and many 19th century people learnt to recite it with pride.

The Women of Mumbles Head

Bring novelists, your notebooks! bring dramatists your pen!
and I'll tell you a single story of what women do for men.
It's only a tale of a lifeboat, of the dying and the dead.
Of a terrible storm and shipwreck, that happened off Mumbles Head.
Maybe you have travelled Wales, sir, and know it north and south.
Maybe you are friends with the natives that dwell in Oystermouth.
It happened, no doubt, that from Bristol you've crossed in a casual way
And have sailed your yacht in the summer, in the blue of Swansea bay.

Well, it isn't like that in the winter, when the lighthouse stands alone,
In the teeth of Atlantic breakers, that form on the face of stone,
It wasn't like that when the hurricane blew, and storm bells rolled or when
There was news of a wreck, and the life-boat, and a desperate way for men.
When in the work did the coxswain shirk? a brave salt was he!
Proud to the bone of as four strong lads as ever had tasted the sea.
Welshman all to the lungs and loins, who, about the coast twas said,
Had saved some hundred lives a piece — at a shilling or so a head!

It didn't go well with the lifeboat! 'twas a terrible storm that blew,
And it snapped the rope in a second that was flung to the drowning crew;
And then the anchor parted — 'twas a tussle to keep afloat!
But the father stuck to the rudder, and the boys to the brave old boat.
Then at last on the poor doom'd lifeboat a wave broke mountains high!
'God help us now!' said the father 'it's over my lads goodbye.'
Half the crew swam seawards! half to the sheltered caves,
But father and sons were fighting death in the foam of the angry waves.

Up at the lighthouse window two women beheld the storm,
And saw in the boiling breakers a figure — a fighting form,
It may be a grey head father, then the women held their breath,
It might be a fair haired brother, who was having a round with death,

It might be a lover, a husband whose kisses were on the lips
Of the women whose love is the life of men, going down to the sea in ships;
They had seen the launch of the lifeboat, then had seen the worst and
more'
Then kissing each other, these women went down from the lighthouse
straight to the shore.

There by the rocks on the breakers these sisters, hand in hand,
Beheld once more that desperate man who struggled to reach the land,
'Twas only aid he wanted to help him across the wave
But what are a couple of women with only a man to save?
What are a couple of women? Well more than three Craven men.
Who stood by the shore with chattering teeth refusing to stir — and then
Off went the women's shawls, sir, in a second they're torn and rent,
Then knotting them into a rope of love, straight into the sea they went!

'Come back!' cried out the lighthouse keeper, 'For God's sake girls, come back!
As they caught the waves on their foreheads, resisting the fierce attack.
'Come back?' moaned the grey haired mother, as she stood by the angry sea,
'If the waves take you, my darlings, there's nobody left to me.'
'Come back!' said the three strong soldiers, who stood faint and pale.
'You'll drown in the face of the breakers! You will fall if you brave the gale!'
'Come back!' said the girls, 'we will not! go tell it to all the town
We'll lose our lives, God willing, before that man shall drown.'

'Give one more knot to the shawls, Bess! Give one strong clutch of your hand!
Just follow me, brave, to the shingle, and we'll bring him safe to land!
Wait for the next wave, darling, only a minute more,
And I'll have him safe in my arms, dear, and we'll drag him safe to the shore.'
Up to the arms in water, fighting it breast to breast,
They caught and saved a brother alive! God bless us we know the rest —
Well many a heart beats stronger, and many a tear was shed,
And many a glass was tossed right off to the Women of Mumbles Head.

The tragedy of this rescue attempt is that the wreck beached at
low water and the rest of the crew were able to scramble over the
rocks to the safety of the lighthouse. Had the lifeboat not put to sea
no lives would have been lost. Instead, four of the crew were lost
including two sons and a son-in-law of the coxswain. Four women
were widowed and fourteen children orphaned.

The Jenkins brothers were buried at Oystermouth Church
where their gravestone can be seen today. Inside the church, on the

north west wall, a brass plaque records that the stained glass window near the pulpit was erected in memory of the four men of the Mumbles Lifeboat who lost their lives on 27 January, 1883. The window depicts the figure of Christ in the upper half and the Mumbles lifeboat, propelled by oars as it would have been in the 1880's, in the lower panel.

Buried Treasure in the River Ogmore

Tales of buried treasure are well known throughout Wales, and of course the County of Glamorgan is no exception. There are numerous legends about the River Ogmore. The waters were considered to contain magical powers and, until the last century were used as a depository for treasure. Why the River Ogmore was made the recipient of so much wealth has now been lost in the mists of time.

The locals believed that, if a person who hoarded money and jewellery died before telling anyone where their wealth was hidden, their spirit would never rest until the treasure was found. But like all good legends, it was not that simple. The hoard had to be found by a 'living hand' and then thrown downstream into the River Ogmore. This ensured the poor tormented spirit would be freed of his earthly bonds and thus rest in peace in the spirit world. If the treasure was thrown upstream the person who threw it in would have no peace himself.

One such story dates from the beginning of the 19th century. One day a ghostly figure, dressed in clothes of a past age, was seen in the village of Newton, two miles from the mouth of the river. The man was pointing towards the dunes of Newton Warren. Eventually, after several sightings, a villager who had been given Holy powers, plucked up the courage to ask him why he was so miserable. The ghost beckoned him and led him to the middle of the dunes where he indicated for the man to dig the sand. He dug as quickly as he could and finally his efforts were rewarded when he uncovered much gold and jewels. Next day the villager took the hoard and threw it downstream into the river as the legend demanded. From that day the ghost was never seen again.

Another tale concerns an old woman from the adjoining parish to Llanilltud Fawr (Llantwit Major). A bad tempered old man, suspected by the neighbours to be a miser who hoarded his money, lived in a cottage owned by the woman. He took no one into his confidence and after his death the woman began to complain that the old man would give her no peace. His ghost appeared day and night and she asked her neighbours what she could do about it. They suggested deacons and elders from the local church should meet in the house. They arrived and began singing and praying but noticed the woman looked strange and perplexed and did not join in. The singing and praying continued getting louder and louder. Suddenly the woman sprang to her feet and shouted excitedly, 'There he is, there he is'. None of the elders could see the old man but told the woman to speak to the ghost. They heard the woman enquire, 'where is it?' but no one heard the reply. Then, going to the large open chimney, she put her hand up and pulled out a bag full of coins. Shouting and struggling with an unseen assailant, the woman bellowed, 'let me go'. Then she hurried from the house and out into the darkness. A few of the more agile church members followed but were only in time to see the woman leap over the stile. They followed but could not see her.

Late that evening the woman returned covered from head to toe in sand and mud. The elders helped her into the cottage and she told them that, when she found the money bag, the old man's spirit seized her and pushed her through the door. Once over the stile, he carried her to the River Ogmore many miles away. There he held her in mid air whilst she undid the bag and dropped the coins downstream into the water. When the last coin had been thrown in the ghost set her down on the muddy river bank, thanked her by saluting and was never seen again.

Treasure at Castell Coch

Above the village of Tongwynglais, six miles north of Cardiff, nests the fairy-tale *Castell Coch* — The Red Castle, so called because of the red brickwork. Perched high on a hill surrounded by a backcloth of trees it stands majestically like something out of a Walt Disney movie. Film makers often use it for shooting medieval location scenes, and *Ivanhoe* was one film shot here. It was restored in the 19th century by two enthusiasts who were passionately in love with the Middle Ages. John Patrick Crichton-Stuart, third Marquess of Bute, who, in his day, was reputed to be the richest man in the world, thanks to a fortune he acquired from the expanding coal port at Cardiff. The architect was William Burges, who studied Middle Age Architecture from books, old manuscripts and extensive travel. He did his best to live up to the period by wearing medieval clothes and sketching on vellum. In 1871, the Marquess asked Billy, as he was called, what could be done with the castle, now a ruin on the Bute estate. The *Castell Coch Report* was an art in itself with many beautiful illustrations. The building of the castle began in 1874 and continued until Burges' death in 1881. The interior was completed over the next 10 years from his drawings and models.

The original castle was built by Gilbert de Clare in 1250 as a fortress to guard the narrow passage to the Taff Gorge against the troublesome Welsh who had retreated to the hills above. It is believed to occupy the site of a former Welsh stronghold which belonged to Ifor ap Meurig — Ifor Bach or little Ifor, so named because of his short stature. He was lord of Senghenydd and a notorious chieftain in Norman times. Ivor often boasted that with just 1200 of his men he could beat 12,000 of any army sent to fight against him. Unfortunately history does not record if anyone did take him up on his offer.

One important prisoner who Ifor Bach is reputed to have kept in the stronhold was William Fitzhamon, Earl of Gloucester, son of Robert Fitzhamon. The story goes that, in 1158, Fitzhamon had seized Ifor's lands. Secretly, in the dead of night, Ifor scaled

Cardiff Castle, despite the castle being guarded by 120 men-at-arms and a great number of archers. He captured the Earl, his Countess and their young son and carried them off to Castell Coch. Ifor released them only on condition that everything taken from him unjustly was returned and he was given additional lands in Blaenau. It was possibly this incident that encouraged the Normans to replace the wooden enclosure of Cardiff Castle with a stronger stone keep.

The romantic aspect of Castell Coch has led to a story told locally that treasure is buried in a massive chest in the grounds and guarded by eagles. But like all well known legends, there are conflicting stories about whose treasure it is.

One story claims that Ifor's immense wealth lies concealed in three huge vaults at the head of a tunnel leading from the castle to Cardiff Castle. It is also believed that three golden eagles sit defending the treasure until the day he returns with his 1200 brave men of Glamorgan to reclaim it.

Another tale dating from 1780 tells of a very poor homeless lady who was allowed to live in a few rooms of the then ruined Castell Coch together with two old servants who were also homeless.

One night the old lady was awakened by a ghost dressed in clothes from the English Civil War period. She was not frightened and spoke gently to the man who immediately vanished through the wall. The ghost appeared before her on subsequent nights but eventually, because the old servants were so scared, the old lady was forced to move. The local people say the ghost was a former owner of the castle, who had filled an iron chest with gold during the upheavals of the Civil War. He buried the treasure in an underground passage, which he wrongly believed led from Castell Coch to Cardiff Castle, and left two eagles to watch over it.

How true these legends are we do not know, but a more recent strange occurrence may set you thinking about the truth of the eagles and treasure. In 1900 a group of men were exploring the underground passages below Castell Coch when two eagles flew at them and fiercely attacked until they were forced to retreat bewildered and disorientated.

However, back above ground, they decided that two birds would not frighten them off and returned with pistols. As soon as they saw the eagles the men fired but once more they were violently attacked. Again they had to retreat.

Undaunted the men returned for a third time now armed with silver bullets which had been blessed by a priest. Again the eagles attacked unmercifully. This time the ground shook and rain came down in torrents into the underground passage. The eagles flew around and with their huge wings, extinguished the men's torches. Now terrified, the men stumbled and scrambled out of the passage followed by the eagles. Somehow they managed to escape with their lives and, it is said, from that day no one has ever attempted to disturb the eagles again.

Dic Penderyn

Although the story of Richard Lewis is well known throughout Wales, no one can recall his name because he will always be remembered as Dic Penderyn after the cottage in which he was born. At the outbreak of the Merthyr riots on 2nd June, 1831 he was a coal miner living in Merthyr Tydfil to where he had moved from his native Aberavon. The riots began with an attack on the house of the clerk to the Court of Requests. The magistrates called in troops and next day a company of the 93rd Highland Regiment arrived. Outside a local inn the soldiers were surrounded by a crowd, among them Dic Penderyn. Inspired by Dic they moved forward, grabbing the soldiers' muskets in an attempt to disarm them. An ugly scene followed, and the soldiers fired into the crowd, killing and wounding a number of people. Several of the soldiers were injured too.

There is no evidence that Dic took part in the rioting, and although he protested his innocence, he was arrested and charged with rioting, and wounding and attacking a soldier, Donald Black. He was tried at Cardiff Assizes but, whilst giving evidence the soldier admitted that, although he recognised the accused as one of the crowd, he could not say for certain if Dic was his attacker. However, two merchants from Merthyr identified Dic as the assailant and, because of their evidence, he was sentenced to death. The execution was fixed for 31st July.

A petition begging for a reprieve was signed by over 10,000 people. A Quaker philanthropist appealed through Lord Brougham, Lord Chancellor to the Home Secretary for clemency for Dic. A two week stay of execution was granted but no further evidence came to light and the verdict upheld.

At 8 o'clock on Saturday 13th August, at the age of 23, Dic Penderyn was publicly hanged at Cardiff Jail. Four ministers who had been with him during his last hours accompanied him to the scaffold.

After the execution his friends were unable to arrange internment at Cardiff because the authorities would not allow a hanged man to be buried in the city.

The following day thousands walked silently as Dic's body was taken through the vale of Glamorgan for burial. At Llantrisant they were again refused permission to bury the body and at Bridgend they were met with yet another denial. Dic's body was then carried to Aberavon where, in the dead of night, it was buried at St Mary's churchyard without a Holy blessing. Outside the churchyard his brother-in-law, the Reverend Morgan Howells, made an emotional speech in which he told the crowd that an ordinary miner, whose life had hardly began, had left a world of cruel injustice. A stone, simply inscribed R.L. 1831, can be seen in the graveyard.

More than forty years later, in 1874, the truth came to light. A Congregational Minister, the Reverend Evan Evans, reported that a man confessed on his deathbed to the wounding of Donald Black and was concerned that he had remained silent whilst an innocent man paid for his crime.

The name of Dic Penderyn, hung for a crime he did not commit during the Merthyr riots, will be remembered forever throughout the mining valleys of Glamorgan.

The Disaster at Tynewydd Colliery

Pit disasters in Wales, particularly in the Rhondda Valley in the 19th century were, sadly, part of every day life. Following one such disaster which occurred just before 4 p.m. on the afternoon of 11 April 1877 at Tynewydd pit a dramatic rescue took 10 days.

The pit shaft was situated where the Rhondda Fawr and the Rhondda Fach meet. Below ground the men were preparing to leave at the end of a day's shift. Sweaty, black faces with white teeth were awaiting their turn to be raised to the surface in small groups.

Thomas Morgan and his sons, Willam and Richard, were still below ground. They put on their jackets, collected their empty food tins and water bottles and made their way to the cage that would lift them to fresh air and daylight. They had only gone a short distance when they were stopped by a rush of air, a sudden torrent of water and a rumble of thunder. Immediately Thomas knew that an explosion had occurred, and shouted to his sons but his voice was drowned by the noise. The water rushed by dislodging rocks and pit props.

They turned around to make their way back and met Edward Williams and William Cassia. Together the five men continued up towards an airway. Behind them the water rushed through the workings searching for an opening and filling the cavity to the roof. The older men were familiar with the geography of the pit and struggled with their thoughts as they tried to find the best way to freedom. But the flood water had risen and their exit to safety was barred.

They retraced their steps, and passed the place where they had entered the airway. With the water creeping up behind them, they came at last to the highest point, a 'hump' in the passage. Now they were trapped with water behind and ahead, as well as pressure in their ears from the compressed air pocket. In their underground tomb they knew there was nothing they could do but sing, wait and pray and so, to pass time, they sang Welsh songs.

The wailing signal which indicated a disaster had brought a crowd of shawled women and off duty miners to the pit head. A roll-call, quickly organised by the miner's owners, revealed 14 men to be missing. In these mining valleys the community spirit was strong, and every miner present volunteered to help with the rescue.

The first rescuers reached the bottom of the pit and found the main level was clear of water. They made their way through the tunnel stopping every 10 to 20 paces to listen for voices or signals from hammers. After travelling for about half a mile they heard the steady thud of a pick. Carefully they made their way towards the sound and soon were signalling through the coal barrier to the trapped men. Experienced trained engineers were called in and it was established that the men were trapped 30 feet below the main roadway. By the following morning the barrier of coal had been reduced to a thin wall and the rescuers now could shout to the miners. Soon rescuers and prisoners were joking with each other. Eventually an engineer warned the miners he was about to break through the barrier. Suddenly there was an explosion as the compressed air tore through the small breach in the wall. The rescuers were blown over. They waited a minute, then struggled to bring out four men and the body of William, who had been hurled forward and killed instantly.

During the night another rescue party fought desperately against time. They heard signals coming from an underground cavern and realised that they were above a stall where Edward o'r Maindy and a 13 year old boy, Robert Rogers, had been cutting coal. They worked hard, sinking a shaft from the main level to the heading below, occasionally stopping to signal to the trapped men. As the night wore on the tapping became fainter and finally stopped. When the rescuers eventually broke through they found the heading full of water and the two trapped men drowned. The bodies could not be recovered until the water level had subsided and, because they knew time was precious and more miners were trapped somewhere below them, they left the bodies where they lay.

At the pithead the Inspector of Mines, Mr R.E. Wales, discussed with other officials how best to rescue the seven men still trapped. An examination of the nearby disused and flooded Hinde pit revealed that the water level had dropped by 100 feet, indicating this to be the source of the flooding at Tynewydd.

A pump was installed speedily at the bottom of Tynewydd shaft and pipes laid to the surface. The rescue team explored the upper-level heading, moving slowly and signalling. By late afternoon they heard the faint tapping in a cavern below. Excitement filtered through to the awaiting crowd above the ground. Finally the men were located about half a mile from the shaft, and a cheer echoed through the valleys as new hope stirred in the hearts of everyone. An additional pump was brought into use and 13,000 gallons of water removed every hour. However, the experts calculated that before the immense volume of water could be removed, the men would die of starvation and exposure.

Meanwhile the inspector asked for divers to join the rescue and in the early hours of 14 April two arrived by special train from London. Their task was not going to be easy because trams, floating timber and rubble blocked the narrow passages, but they were fired with determination, driven on by the women, holding young babies or clinging to the iron gates of the mine. Slowly they made their way down but were forced to return. Disappointment swept through the valleys but the rescuers were determined to have another go. The pumps were started up again and by Sunday afternoon the flood was receding. Before long the team would make its final attack on the 120 ft barrier which separated the men from safety.

In their underground tomb, day was no different to night. The miners were cold, hungry, and drank the filthy water to quench their thirst. Two had earlier drowned attempting to swim to safety.

By Monday the water level had dropped sufficiently for the rescue party to make a last desperate attempt to reach the men. In the afternoon the first team, under Inspector Wales' direction, began to tunnel through the coal seam. Progress was slow and dangerous and after four hours they had only descended five yards. The pumping and digging continued and by the following afternoon they were half way through the seam. As they moved nearer to the miners the rescuers began to consider how best they could break into the compressed air filled chamber without killing the men. They finally decided to build airtight doors across the tunnel and to use the compressed air inside the airlock to equalise the pressure on either side of the barrier. At seven the following evening the rescuers were close enough to shout to the men. By mid-day Friday 20 April, to the cheers of a jubilant crowd, the last of the survivors emerged from the darkness.

There have been many disasters in the history of the Welsh coalfields — some suffering a substantial loss of life — but the Tynewydd disaster will be remembered for the 10 days of suspense, the courage of the waiting women, and the sheer determination of the rescuers. The finest accolade came when Queen Victoria made the following announcement:

'The Albert Medal hitherto bestowed only for gallantry in saving life at sea, shall be extended to similar actions on land, and the first medals struck for the purpose shall be conferred on the heroic rescuers of the Welsh miners.'

On 7 August 1877, the London Gazette published the names of the 24 men on whom this honoured was bestowed.

Llanilltud Fawr and the Story of 'One A-Waiting'

Even today the town of Llanilltud Fawr (Llantwit Major) has an old-world appearance that transports a visitor back in time. The numerous picturesque thatched roofed cottages are a sight not to miss but its narrow crooked streets are a nightmare. Many motorists have found themselves heading out of the town on the wrong road. Llanilltud has played host to many races from earliest man and has the distinction of being the oldest University town in the United Kingdom.

The first Christian school or university was founded in 68 A.D. by the Welsh Princess Eurgain when Llantwit was known as *Caer Wrgan* or *Caer Gwrgan*. It was known as *Bangor Eurgain* — the school or seminary of Eurgain. In 322 A.D. the school was destroyed by Irish pirates but was re-established some 47 years later by Emperor Theodosius and became known as *Bangor Tedwr* — the college of Theodosius.

When St Illtyd became head of the school the name changed yet again, this time to *Bangor Illtyd*.

Llanilltyd — the church of Illtyd was known as 'Fawr' — the word Major is used to distinguish it from two other villages, near Caerphilly, also in Glamorgan.

There is a strong Scandinavian link which can be seen in the style of the farmhouses and also in its inhabitants. Unlike other towns in the southern part of Glamorgan, the people speak mainly English and not Welsh. Also there is an unusual connection with a Scandinavian folk tale known as 'One-a-waiting'. This is told in Llanilltud, Stockholm and Copenhagen, but nowhere else in the world.

Llanilltud's version of the legend tells of a group of men who went to Cowbridge fair, about 9 miles away, to combine business with pleasure. When they arrived at the fair they separated and, after an enjoyable time, met as arranged and started for home. They began telling each other about their days' exploits when they realised one of the party was missing. Frantically they counted heads.

'Yes indeed,' one of them said. 'Seven of us started out this morning, and now there are only six. There's one a-waiting.'

'What shall we do?' they said in unison.

'We can't leave one behind,' said one.

'We must go back,' said another. They agreed and so back towards Cowbridge they tramped, asking everyone they met if they had seen a man walking along the road. The answer was always the same, no.

Finally they met a friend who stopped and asked them why they looked so worried.

'Seven of us left this morning and now we are six. We are one a-waiting.'

The friend counted for himself and found the party was complete. Suddenly it dawned on them, each had forgotten to include himself.

Interestingly a similar version of this story exists in Denmark. The tale, 'The Noses', is taken from the 'Molbo Tales' which was first published in Copenhagen in 1887 by Professor Fausboll.

'Once upon a time the arithmetical knowledge of the Molbo's was put to a strong test. They wanted to count how many they were. They knew that they were seven when they left from home that day, but every one of them could not count more than six present, as he who counted the others always forgot to include himself. When they had racked their brains for a long time, and could not make the number more than six, although they could not see that any of the party was missing. They asked a traveller passing by to help them solve this difficulty. He led them to a big soft cow-turd, and instructed them to lay themselves down flat upon the ground round it, all facing inwards. He then asked them to put their noses deep into it, and then count the holes. This they did, and now they were able, each and all, to count the seven holes.'

Hidden Gold at Llanrhidian

For as long as records show, the inhabitants of north-west Gower have been telling stories about hidden treasure. If the tales are true then every part of Gower must hide a hoard of treasure. For generations Gowerians have searched the caves, hunted through the marshland leaving no stone unturned, but always the quest has ended in disappointment.

Then one night, an elderly cleric had a strange dream in which he found himself walking through woods and down a path to a hidden cove on the south side of the shore. In the sand before him he saw the imprints of a cloven footed animal which led towards the rocks and into a cave. Either side of the entrance was lit with a lantern. He could hear Welsh lullabies being played on a harp inside and, as he stood listening, a cleft in the rocks opened inviting him into an Aladdin's cave of treasure. The cleric woke abruptly and, quivering with excitement immediately recalled every little detail of the dream.

He knew the area well and the following evening set off to retrace the journey, his man-servant following behind with a lantern and a small bardic harp. They hurried through the woods, and then along the narrow winding path that led to the cove. In front of him the clergyman saw the imprints in the sand, just as they had appeared in his dream, and became excited. Soon they were at the entrance to the cave and the cleric instructed his servant to play the harp.

'Play, play on,' he urged when he saw the cleft in the rock slowly opening.

Inside the cave they found two heaps of gold, each guarded by a gnome who was fast asleep. The clergyman gasped in disbelief, he had never seen so much wealth in his life before. His servant came hurrying over to his side. Together they filled their pockets with as much gold as they could carry. Once they emerged from the cave the rock closed behind them. Each swore the other to secrecy and they went back to the cave on a number of occasions to collect more treasure.

On one particular night they followed their usual routine but once inside the cave the treasure hunters felt an eerie presence. The cave felt cold and the gnome who usually guarded the gold was no where to be seen. Uneasy they knelt down and began to fill their pockets with gold. Suddenly they heard the stone door slam behind them and they were never seen in Llanrhidian again.

It is said that if you find a lonely cave and hear a strange haunting tune coming from within, you will find two ghosts of long ago trying to escape from their golden tomb.

The Mysteries of Kenfig

Between Porthcawl and Port Talbot lies a vast waste of dreary flat wet land, broken by sand dunes and the sea. According to legend this was once a land of green meadows where cattle grazed. Later the ancient city of Kenfig was built on the site, but was buried when the area became engulfed by sand and sea.

According to history the inhabitants made a road or causeway, known as Heol-las, meaning the green or leafy way, more than two thousand years ago. In turn the Romans used the old trackway, which they are believed to have called Via Julia Maritima. Two old bridges near Kenfig were erected by the Romans and are still in use today.

On this road was built the first town of Kenfig and it formed part of the lands owned by the Welsh lord of Glamorgan, Iestyn ap Gwrgan. It was once no more than a collection of wooden huts edged by marshy lands — hence the original Welsh name *Cefn-y-ffignon*, meaning a ridge on a marsh. When Robert Fitzhamon defeated Iestyn during the Invasion of Glamorgan, he built a motte and bailey castle on the site of Iestyn's former castle. Soon a medieval town grew around Kenfig and the Normans developed it, intending to turn it into a main trading centre for mid Glamorgan. However, it seems that the success of Kenfig was doomed from the start.

It suffered badly from the raids of the disinherited Welsh Lords of Afon, especially one called Morgan Gam. During these raids the town was burned down on several occasions. The inhabitants built a barricade around it to try and save it but again it was destroyed. Even Llywelyn the Great attacked it and later Owain Glyndŵr destroyed it completely. The town refused to die and was again rebuilt and gained parliamentary privileges. Around 1300 a series of storms hit the south coast of Wales followed by periods of drifting sand. Slowly it became impossible to live at Kenfig and, by the end of the 15th century, it had become a ghost town as people moved to safer towns further inland. In 1536, the writer Leland in his *Itinerary* spoke of Kenfig as 'a little village on the est side of

Kenfig and a castel booth in ruine and almost shokid (choked) and devourid with the sandes that the Severn Se there castith up.'

Of course being Wales it is impossible to have a buried city without a legend, especially when a large stretch of water, like Kenfig pool, is situated near by. Strangely this pool is only 1,000 yards from the sea yet there is no trace of salt water in it.

The legend recalls that a peasant boy living in the village of Kenfig fell in love with the daughter of the Norman Earl of Clare. He asked her to marry him but she refused because he was poor. It seems that, even then, money and wealth was just as important to some girls. To win over her affections he turned to crime and killed and robbed a local lord. With his newly acquired wealth he bought grander clothes for himself and showered the girl with gifts. Suitably impressed, she finally agreed to marry him.

During the wedding reception, as the guests were enjoying the feast, a frightening voice was heard over the merriment.

'Vengeance will come.' It repeated the warning several times. The guests stopped and listened and then asked the obvious questions. Why? When? To the first query there was no reply, but to the second the voice bellowed, 'Vengeance will come at the end of the ninth generation.'

Too drunk to fully understand they laughed. One said there was no need to fear because 'all of us will be under the earth long before then'. They all laughed again before continuing with the celebrations.

According to the legend they all lived until the ninth generation when the murderer's descendent was born, and grew up in the village. Then one day a young man arrived at Kenfig, announced he was the ninth descendant of the murdered man and settled into the village. Presently, as the cock crowed, a voice was heard clearly over the town. It spoke the same sentence three times.

'Vengeance has come.'

'On whom has it come?' asked the villagers in unison.

'On him and his who slew my ancestor of the ninth generation.'

Remembering the old legend the villagers fled indoors in fear of what would happen. Suddenly there was a great rush of water, and all that could be seen of the village was three smoking chimney tops. On the surface of the newly formed lake a pair of gloves floated to the feet of the murdered man's descendant. He picked them up and saw that they bore the name and coat of arms of the man murdered nine centuries earlier. A voice was heard in the sky praising God that justice had now been done.

It is claimed even to this day that, when the waters are still and clear, the houses of the old town can be seen at the bottom of the lake. Also, if you listen carefully, the bells of the old church ring out before a violent storm.

Sadly this legend cannot be true as old maps show the old town of Kenfig to be some distance from the lake and so the houses couldn't possibly be under the water. However, as the villagers of Kenfig will testify, historical fact has not dispelled the countless stories relating to the buried town of Kenfig.

Guto Nyth Brân

One of the greatest runners in Wales, Griffith Morgan was born in 1700 at Llwyncelyn in the old farmhouse of *Nyth Brân* - the crow or raven's nest. Hence he was given the nickname, Guto Nyth Brân, Guto being short for Griffith. The farmhouse stood on the slopes of Troedrhiwtrwyn near the Great Western colliery in the Rhondda valley.

He grew up to be an extremely fast runner and there are many tales about Guto, no doubt largely embroidered. It is claimed he slept in a dung heap to strengthen his legs and often would pace himself against hares and foxes. He was able to beat anyone, whether over mountainous or flat ground.

According to legend, if his mother sent him to Llantrisant or Aberdare, he would ask her as he was leaving, to put the kettle on the fire for a cup of tea on his return. He would set off, cover the twelve miles, deliver the message or buy goods and return before his mother could make the tea.

One day his father told him to take the dog and bring the sheep down from the mountains for shearing.

'I won't need the dog,' said Guto and set off. Soon he returned.

'Did you have any trouble catching them?' asked his father.

'None at all,' replied Guto. 'Just one gave me a little trouble. That one there, the strange looking one, the reddish grey one, but I caught it in the end.'

'But . . . but, that's a hare,' exclaimed his father. 'How on earth did you catch a hare?'

'Easy' said Guto, 'I caught her as she rose from behind the ferns on the mountainside.'

Guto sometimes ran with the local Llanwynno hunt and had no difficulty in keeping up over moors and mountains. He would often catch the fox by its tail, long before the hounds came into sight. On one occasion he chased the fox all the way to Cardigan before eventually catching it. By now darkness was approaching and Guto and the hound were too tired to make the journey home. A gentleman made Guto comfortable for the night and the following day he ran several races against the man's horse and won every time. The gentleman told him that the horse had lost him a considerable sum of money in a race against another man's horse. Guto being grateful for the man's hospitality decided to repay him. He offered to run against the other man's horse in the hope that he could win back some of the man's lost money.

The race was arranged for the following day and Guto ran a magnificent race beating the horse by several yards. But Guto was not the only victor as the man won back all the money he had lost and more!

One of Guto's most ardent fans was a woman called *Siân the Shop* who had won a substantial amount of money betting on Guto's races. In one race he had beaten an English army captain over four miles to win the £500 prize. An Englishman called Price, thinking Guto could not repeat this performance, challenged him to another race, this time over twelve miles, for a larger sum of money. Guto and his friends had no hesitation in accepting the offer.

The race attracted much publicity and hundreds of pounds were laid as bets on both men. Guto's friends and supporters went along to cheer and Sian the Shop followed behind struggling with an apron full of gold sovereigns to gamble on Guto winning.

The two men left Newport together but Guto took his time and stopped a few times to shake hands and talk to supporters, falling further and further behind. Eventually he remembered Sian the shop and all the sovereigns she had placed on him winning. Guto started to run in earnest and was soon gaining on the Englishman, but some of Price's supporters spread glass on the road to slow him down. This did not deter him and he leapt over the glass and ran on. As he came to the steep slope leading to Bedwas church, the finishing line, he caught up with Price and made a jibe about him running too slow to win the race. For a time both men ran together then Guto surged forward and crossed the finishing line in 53 minutes.

Siân had won two apronfuls of gold sovereigns and, being excited, ran up to Guto slapped him on the back shouting 'Well done. Long live Guto Nyth Brân'

Unfortunately, in the excitement, Siân had forgotten that he had run a hard race and his heart was beating faster because of his final efforts to win. To everyone's horror he suddenly crumbled to the floor.

The back slapping had proved too much for him and he died of a heart attack at the age of thirty-seven.

Guto was buried in Llanwynno churchyard. A stone with an inscribed heart etched on it was placed on the grave to record how he had died and can be seen today.

The White Ladies of Glamorgan

Throughout Wales there are numerous tales of the appearance of *Y Ladi Wen* — the white lady — and Glamorgan has its fair share of lady ghosts too. We have tales from, amongst others, Aberavon, Gower, Ewenny, Bishopston, Llantrisant, Ogmore and Cardiff.

The White Lady of Ogmore Castle guards treasure kept under the floorboards of the tower, and once she even allowed a man to search for, and find, an old pot full of golden guineas. She told him he could keep his nest egg provided he left the rest for her. However the man was not content with his pot of gold. On his way out of the castle he dug up a stone which he used to mark the spot where the money lay hidden. One night greed got the better of him. He ignored his promise to the White Lady and returned to the castle. After a little searching he found the marker stone, removed it and filled his pockets with the gold. As he was about to walk away the White lady appeared and accused him of taking her gold. The man denied it but she made him take off his coat, shake it thoroughly and the money fell to the floor. Furious at his disobedience she lunged at him tearing him with her claws. Despite being badly injured he escaped and arrived home in a sorry state. No one would believe his story of Y ladi Wen and, despite his denials accused him of being in a drunken brawl. Not long after the man was struck down by a mysterious illness and wasted away. Before he died he told the truth about his wealth and spoke of his illness being the 'White Lady's Revenge'.

In another tale the White Lady of Rhiwsaeson, near Llantrisant, needed to kiss a newborn unbaptised baby to release her from her earthly bonds. One evening, she went up to a local farm labourer as he was returning from work and told him his wife was about to give birth. She then asked him to bring the child to her as soon as it was born so that she could be saved. The man was frightened and went to the local parson who advised him to have the child christened before taking him out. The man returned to the white lady, child in arms, and, as they approached, she began to wring her hands and shout that the conditions of her redemption had not been fulfilled.

In Bishopston village in Gower another white lady frequented an old manor house, the home of the rector who had lived there alone since his wife had died. One night, as he was on his way to bed, he saw the figure of a woman dressed in white moving silently through the hall. He stopped for a closer look but she had disappeared. Looking at the moonlight shafting though the window he dismissed it as a figure of his imagination. The next night the same thing happened and on many more occasions she appeared in different rooms. The first time he saw her as a misty haze but each time she appeared she became more real and the rector became increasingly frightened. After a while the ghost's presence was accompanied by a terrifying noise, a swirling wind rushing through the house, furniture moving and curtains swaying from side to side. The rector became so petrified that, as soon as something eerie began to happen, he would flee from the house, often in his nightwear, and stay on the common until he could pluck up enough courage to return. Sometimes the villagers would join him on the common and return with him to the house. Each time they found the house still and undisturbed and eventually people began to suspect that he was going senile and imagining the events.

One day a gypsy woman called at the house to peddle her wares. When the rector opened the door she looked straight past him to the dusky halfway with fear in her eyes. She took a few steps backwards.

"*Ysbrydion . . . Ysbrydion*" — Ghosts . . . Ghosts" she muttered as she rushed into the garden. The rector hurried after her and, when he caught up with her, she told him the only way to free himself from the White Lady was to use the bell and candle test. According to superstition the haunting spirit preferred darkness and was angered by the sound of bells. Legend has it that the ghost would sometimes brave the sound of the bells and attempt to blow out the candles. If all flames were extinguished before the 12th stroke of midnight the ghost could not be driven from the house and would remain forever. But if just one candle continued to burn, the ghost would be defeated and the earthly victors would have to give her a task to keep her away from the house forever.

The rector arranged for 12 local churchmen to come to the manor after dark. Twelve candles and twelve handbells were placed on the scrubbed kitchen table. When midnight approached they lit the candles and rang the handbells.

At the stroke of midnight strange noises could be heard, furniture moved and a cold wind blew through the house. The cleric's were tempted to flee but drew courage from one another and decided to help the rector. Suddenly they saw a flowing white robe and the defiant eyes of the ghost glowing in the dimness. In a rage she ran from candle to candle trying to blow them out. The clerics rang the bells, chanted louder and prayed harder. As the chimes struck the white lady became more confused and alarmed and, at the last stroke, with the candles still flickering she backed into a corner to await their final judgement.

One cleric, acting as spokesman, banished the white lady to a point in Caswell Bay where she was to build a castle of sand to withstand the force of the waves. She was never seen in the manor house again. But local people will tell you that if you look out to the middle of Caswell Bay there is a strange stirring in the sand. Some say it is an inland stream meeting the sea, others claim it is a ghost busily digging in the sand to make her castle. They will tell you also that the wind swirling up the winding Caswell Valley is the White Lady rushing around in a vain attempt to stop the flowing tide washing away her castle.

Another ghost, the White Lady of Ewenny, is usually seen between White Lady's Meadow and White Lady's Lane pointing towards Ewenny with a mournful expression upon her face.

One day a man was crossing the marshy fields when he saw her wringing her hands in great distress. He managed to pluck up enough courage to speak to her and asked if there was anything he could do to help her escape from the earthly bonds. She told him to hold tightly with both wrists to her arms and not to let go of her whatever happened. The man tried his hardest to concentrate but suddenly was distracted by a dog barking. Momentarily he looked around and let go of her hands. The White Lady's face twisted and she screamed at the man. 'Now I shall be bound for another seven years'. Then she vanished and the man made his way home badly shaken by the event.

The villagers of Ewenny believe the White lady is the soul of a tormented lady who long ago committed a misdeed, possibly in connection with some treasure — hence the pointing of a finger. Some have even mentioned that they know where the treasure is hidden, but are too afraid to retrive it. Even today, in some Glamorgan villages, fear for Y Ladi Wen runs high.

Taffy was a Welshman

The anti-Welsh rhyme 'Taffy was a Welshman' must have angered and annoyed the Welsh people for centuries, but once fully understood it can be seen in a different light, even with a sense of humour and bravado.

Taffy was a Welshman.
Taffy was a thief,
Taffy came to our house,
And stole a leg of beef.
I went to Taffy's house,
Taffy was in bed;
I picked up a chopper
And chopped off his head.

The origin of his old doggerel is believed to be from the period just after the Norman invasion of Glamorgan. However, it could date from between 757 to 796 A.D. when Offa, King of Mercia, built the great dyke which bears his name and behind which the Welsh retreated.

During the Norman invasion the Welsh were driven back into the hills by the superior force who swept inland from the coast. With their animals, hunting grounds, cattle and common pasture lands taken, the Welsh resorted to swift and heroic raids on the enemy in order to stave off hunger and support their families. The old rhyme tells of cattle raids — hence the leg of beef followed by the retaliation raid in which Taffy was killed.

Later the raids became more predatory and less war-like. To the Norman and English now living in the lowlands these raids were looked upon as nothing less than bare-faced robbery — hence the jibe about Taffy being a thief. To the Welsh, however, still feeling the sting from their defeat, these forays were seen as attempts to retrieve from the conquerors what was rightly theirs.

There are numerous tales of blatant cattle and sheep thefts as the Welsh attempted to get back at '*yr hen elyn*' — the old enemy. We can all imagine the scenario. A Norman wife has just spit-roasted a delicious leg of beef for the family evening meal whilst Taffy lurks, hidden, in the vicinity awaiting his opportunity to pounce. When the wife turns her back for a second, Taffy slips by unnoticed and makes off with the families' supper. Later that night, as Taffy passes around the joint of beef, we can imagine the tales of bravery being elaborated as they are told around the flickering embers of the fire.

One historian writing during this period recorded that attempts were made to make peace with the Welsh on many occasions, but they could not forget the attack on their land:

'Messages were sent them offering Conditions of Peace, yet malice and Rancour soe boyled in their Stomackes they would not heare thereof, thinking it more honest to dye by dint of sword than to suffer unrevenged'.

The Welsh have always been a proud nation and we can only surmise that any attempt at peace would have been looked upon as an endeavour to undermine their culture.

The Ghost of Llanfeuthin

Llanfeuthin is a hamlet, in the district of Llancarvan, which was once the home of a monastic brotherhood. St Cadog is believed to be the founder of the St Meuthin monastery, named after a holy hermit who baptised him and later became his tutor. At Llanfeuthin there are many legends handed down through generations about a Welshman who had been walled up in one of the thick double walls of the monastery. There are two versions of this story, both worth re-telling so that the reader can draw his or her conclusions.

The first tells of a Welsh prince who once had been a student at the monastery. As a General he had been defeated in battle in North Wales. Pursued by his enemies, he decided to flee south for protection. When he arrived at Llanfeuthin he found workmen building an unusually thick wall and asked them if he could hide between the double walls until it was safe. They agreed and helped him into position, leaving enough unmortated space for him to breathe. Shortly his enemies arrived in the village. They began searching for the Welsh prince and, when they couldn't find him, became very angry. The masons, terrified that if it were found they had helped the prince they would be killed, mortared up the breathing space, leaving the Welshman to his fate.

In the other version the Welshman is not only a prince and a General, but also a bard with the bardic name of *Aneurin Gwawdrydd* — meaning the golden one of the free song. He is also the author of a 7th century Epic poem — *Y Gododdin*, about the battle of Catraeth which took place in Scotland in 603 A.D We know from historical documents that Aneurin was present at this battle although he did not actually fight. In this version of the story he was involved in a conflict in North Wales and killed the General of the opposing side. Again, being a former pupil of Llanfeuthin, he fled there for safety and was hidden and cared for by a monk. Sadly for Aneurin, it is reputed that the monk assigned to look after him was either a great friend or a relation of the general whom Aneurin had killed. One day, whilst chopping wood, the monk quarrelled with the bard, and cut off his leg. Consequently he bled to death and, to hide his murder, the monk hid the body between the two walls of the monastery.

The truth of either story is uncertain but a most interesting discovery was made. During the suppression of the monasteries the old monastery was converted, first into a private manor house and later, by the Ecclesiastical Commissioners, into a farm house of which Mr William Loughor was the new tenant. Some time after moving in he needed a larger dairy and decided the spacious cellar would be ideal. To give additional light he chose to open up the north wall but the workmen assigned to the job found it

particularly difficult because of the thickness. Eventually, when they had broken through about eight foot of the double wall, they came across the skeleton of a young man, his brilliant red hair still preserved, and one leg cut off below the knee. Around the skeleton lay heaps of grey dust believed to be the remains of his clothes and, where the one leg bone had rested, they found a perfectly preserved shoe.

Because the story of the walled up man was well known in the area the workmen immediately knew the skeleton must have been that of Aneurin who was reputed to have had a mass of red hair. The remains were blessed, carefully placed in a coffin and buried in a tomb.

Of course all good tragic stories must have a ghost too, and this tragedy is no exception. The ghost, a woman dressed all in white, was said to be the wife of the Welshman who had been walled up. She was seen mostly in the cellar, but also wandered into the house and up and down the stairs looking for her husband. She was well known in the area and was often the subject of a practical joke played on the supersitious villagers.

There is an amusing tale about a former tenant of Llanfeuthin, who was visited by the ghost night after night. The farmer was plagued by the ghost who appeared to be unusually strong for a spirit because she would pull the bed clothes off him, annoy him and beat him until he was black and blue. Eventually the farmer had enough and decided to rid himself of the ghost. A colt with a whitish head, belly and front legs had recently died and he decided to use the hide to frighten his unwelcome guest. First he cut a long narrow strip from the hoof of one leg then up to and across the head and down to the hoof of the other leg. The rest he cut into narrow strips and wove together to make a bag large enough to catch the ghost. Through the neck he threaded the long narrow strip and fixed the opening of the bag across the open cellar door. The farmer thought the ghost would become so angry at seeing or being caught in the bag that she would flee for good. The next night the ghost appeared and when she saw the bag made a hasty retreat. The farmer was delighted, thinking that he had rid himself of the trickster for good but the following night she returned and beat him worse than ever. However, it served its purpose because the farmer was never troubled by the 'ghost' again.

The farmer was a Welshman and a bard and like all poetic Welshmen wrote his experiences down in verse form. It reads as follows, although most of the poetic beauty is lost in the translation:

The Ghost of Llanveithin

'When I was a stripling
Living in Llanveithin,
There was a white lady
There and around the building;

Her dress was of white silk, without a spot,
And her movements remarkably quick,
So that her gown made such a rustle
As a strong wind makes passing through holes.
I made a large bag with four throngs
Of the hide of a yellow-bellied, white foot colt;
I place it at the door of the cellar,
To catch the grand ghost of Llanveithin
For thus making it I was punished;
She came to my bed that night,
She pinched squeezed, and bared me,
And kept me stripped until I was nigh perished.'

Snakes and Winged Serpents

Stories of snakes and winged serpents, or dragons, are common and it seems that, with many references to snakes being generous to human beings, the Vale of Glamorgan was a favoured spot for these creatures.

One story concerns a large snake with a crown on its head. Every morning and evening near Penmark it would appear before a farmer's daughter and she would give it some warm milk to drink. This went on for months, until one day the snake did not appear and the girl became concerned for its safety. Then she noticed a gold ring on the spot where the snake usually sat. She kept the ring and wore it on her wedding day. In time she became very wealthy and was convinced that her good fortune had something to do with the ring, which she considered had special powers. Many years later when she lay dying she made her daughter promise to wear the ring after her death. Either by accident or design the ring was buried with the mother and from then on the daughter's luck changed for the worse. It is said that often she cursed her bad luck saying it was because she had buried the ring with her mother.

In another tale a snake was responsible for curing a child of scurvy. The condition had broken out in a few of the farmhouses around the St Nicholas area of the Vale of Glamorgan and the infected people were placed in quarantine in an effort to contain the disease.

One of those affected was an eight year old girl who was banished to the orchard to eat her bread and milk in isolation. Over a period of time she became friendly with a few snakes and would sit under her favourite apple tree and share her meal with them. One day her father brought her meal to the orchard and noticed the snakes slithering towards her. From behind a tree he watched in silence as one lifted its head as though it was studying the child's face and then slid away. Shortly it returned with two leaves in its mouth which it dropped besides the other snakes. The girl put down her bowl and laid full length on the ground. Then the snakes started to crush the leaves in their mouths and then, using saliva, began to apply the leaves to the girl's face and arms. Eventually the last snake slid away and the father approached his daughter who, seeing his puzzled look, explained that the snakes had licked her twice before. Within three days she was cured and her father told the doctor what had happened. Convinced they knew what the leaves looked like the two men set off in search but could not find them.

Even more unbelievable stories are told about winged serpents and for one we must travel to Penllyn castle near Cowbridge. An old man living at the castle said that winged serpents haunted and terrorised the woods. When they were at rest they would coil up and appeared to be covered by jewels. Left alone they would eventually glide away sparkling all over. If angered they would fly over people's head with wings outstretched and eyes shining. The old man said his father and uncle were forced to kill many winged serpents because they were 'as bad as foxes for stealing poultry' and, it is claimed because of this, the serpents eventually were wiped out.

A woman who visited Penmark as a young girl also described the winged serpents in the same way and told a tale about the 'king and queen' serpents who frequented the woods around Beaupre, near St Hilary. The older people of the area told her that wherever a winged serpent was found, she would find buried treasure nearby. One day her grandfather, who had met a winged serpent in the woods at Porthkerry Park, decided to catch one. He awaited all day with his brother until finally one appeared. They shot and wounded it, but despite its injury it rose up and attacked the two men. Although men and creature were hurt, the battle continued until finally the brothers killed the serpent. The old woman said she could remember the skin and feathers being proudly displayed in her grandfather's home, much to her grandmother's annoyance. When he died, sadly they were thrown away.

The Enchanting Lakes of Glamorgan

Wales' most famous story about a lady of a lake is the Lady of Llyn y Fan Fach in Carmarthenshire, but Glamorgan has its tales as well.

One is about a golden haired mermaid like lady who lived at *Llyn Fawr* — the Big Lake, in the Rhondda valley. Early in the morning often she was seen combing her long golden hair besides the banks of the lake. As soon as she saw anyone approaching she would dive into the lake and vanish from view. It is said that if a stone is thrown an invisible fairy would catch it before it touched the water so as not to harm or disturb the lady.

Another lady lived at Llyn y Forwyn — the Maiden's Pool, situated between a farmhouse called *Rhondda Fechan* — Little Rhondda — and the Vale of Safrwch. The lake is in the parish of Ystrad Dyfodwg, and is known locally as Llyn Nelferch. This story is very similar to that told about the lady of Llyn y Fan Fach.

One day a young man who lived with his mother on a farm close to the lake saw the lady sitting by the waters edge combing her hair, although some say she was rowing across the lake in a golden boat with a golden oar. The farmer fell in love with her at first sight and approached her but she dived into the water. However, he refused to give up and tried several times, each with the same result

Eventually he consulted a wise man in the area who told him to tempt her with bread and cheese. From Midsummer Eve until the end of the year, the farmer offered her the food but she refused. On the anniversary of the day they had first met, he went to the lake with seven loaves and a full round of cheese. He waited all day and at midnight placed the food on the lake. This must have had the desired affect because we are told that the lady agreed to become his wife on condition that he did not disagree with her on three separate occasions. If he did then she would end the relationship and return to the lake taking all her possessions with her. For a while everything went well.

One day an old neighbour died. The farmer was surprised to see his wife so sad and weeping for the man who was not even a relative. He told her it was a happy release as life had become a burden to him. She replied that she was grieving because, for his earthly misdeeds, the man was going to suffer everlasting misery in the next world.

Their second disagreement occurred when the wife began laughing and rejoicing instead of being upset at the death of their own infant son. Her husband reprimanded her but she said she was happy because their child had passed from this wicked world into a far better world full of peace and happiness.

There is no record of what their third argument was over, but whatever it was it must have annoyed the lady greatly, because the lady of the lake left her husband and returned to her watery home taking her cattle and processions with her.

Another curious lake legend is connected with Crumlyn, a quaint village near Briton Ferry, which is said to cover the old town of Swansea. The story goes that when St Patrick was returning to Ireland he was persecuted here by his fellow countrymen. He was a fiery Welshman, born in 385 A.D. and believed to have been somewhere in the west — some say Glamorgan. They recognised St Patrick and accused him of abandoning Wales in favour of Ireland. They began to beat him whereupon he transformed the men into fishes, the women into fairies and drowned their town. It is said St Patrick ordered that the sun would only shine on the dark waters of the lake for one week in a whole year, and judging by the dismal area now, it appears that his prophecy has come true. It is also said that when the wind is blowing, if a person stands facing the lake and his clothes are touched with the spray, he will be attracted to the water and will need considerable will-power to stop himself from being sucked into the water.

Dr William Price
The Man who cremated his Baby

One of the most famous eccentric Welsh characters must be Dr William Price, a medical practitioner who lived in Llantrisant. He was born in 1900 and took his doctorate at the Royal College of Surgeons in 1821, returning to Wales to practice among those who needed him most. He achieved notoriety thanks to his peculiar actions. He was an ardent student of druidism and called himself the 'Archdruid of Wales', often conducting Druidic ceremonies at the Rocking Stone on Pontypridd Common. He also believed in reincarnation and, when Helena Blavatsky founded the Theosophical Society in 1875, Dr Price wrote to her claiming to be her father in a previous existence some 10,000 years earlier. Helena admitted the logic of this claim and enrolled him in the Society without fee.

William often dressed in green plaid trousers and coat, scarlet vest, and a cap of fox skin with a tail that hung down his back, although when roaming his native Welsh hills he was usually to be found in his birthday suit. He was an ardent sun worshipper and nudist who was followed by a bevy of naked young ladies. He did not believe in marriage because he considered this chained women like slaves to their masters but this did not stop him from fathering many children.

But for all his eccentricities Dr Price is best remembered as a pioneer of cremation. When he was 83 he went to live with a village girl and fathered another child which he named *Iesu Grist* — Jesus Christ. When the child died in 1884 at the age of five months, he wrapped the body in cloth and placed it in a barrel containing paraffin oil to burn it near his home with no Christian ceremony. It was only the speedy arrival of the police that prevented the cremation from taking place and saved the Doctor from the fury of the people.

Dr Price was arrested and charged with attempting to obstruct the course of an inquest by burning a body and for attempting to dispose of a body by burning when the law required that it should be buried in hallowed ground. He was tried at Cardiff Assizes before Mr Justice Stephenson. Doctor Price defended himself successfully on the first count, triumphantly producing the coroner's certificate to prove an inquest had been held and the child had died of natural causes.

On the second charge, he challenged the judge and jury to show him the legislation that made burning of a body illegal. The minister of the church at Llantrisant was called as witness and testified that the Church required the body of any baptised infant to be committed to hallowed ground.

'The Church is not the law,' snapped Price who looked impressive in a long white robe embroidered with cabalistic signs. He continued to speak in a language he claimed was the tongue of the ancient bards of Wales. The judge threatened him with contempt of court and he was removed until tempers had cooled. When he returned to the courtroom he told the judge he had no wish to offend but, because he had been appointed by God as the power among the Druids he was superior therefore in authority to any member of the Christian Church, a much younger institution. He concluded by stating that it was the judge who was at fault, and not him.

Next came a succession of witnesses to testify to his skills as a doctor and to his eccentric behaviour. Dr Price, who had now shed his robe, sat in his usual colourful coat, trousers and waistcoat as though he was hearing someone else's misdeeds.

As regards his skills as a doctor, the people of Llantrisant had a love hate relationship with him. They were quick to call upon him for treatment, but his oddities angered and frightened them. Several women testified that 'he was as gentle as a bird' during their confinements, and one man expressed his praise at the anaesthetic properties of the brandy Dr Price administered during a leg amputation following a pit accident. Finally the case was dismissed on payment of a farthing costs and, true to his style, Dr Price had a medal struck to commemorate the occasion.

He died in January 1893, at the age of 93, and, in accordance with his wishes, his body was cremated on the summit of a hill to the west of the town known as Caerlan fields. He wished his body to be burnt publicly, sitting in an ancient chair on top of two tons of coal like a Guy Fawkes effigy. Permission had to be sought but, because the Home Office was still prevaricating about cremation, this was refused. Instead the corpse was shrouded in a coffin first.

The ceremony was carried out by surpliced clergymen in the presence of some five to six thousand people who had paid three pence each to see the event. Before the day was over thousands more had flocked to the town as the news spread. It is claimed that this was the first public cremation in the country and a tablet to commemorate the event was laid in Llantrisant by the Cremation Society and the Federation of British Cremation Authorities.

Glamorgan's Hounds of Hell

Animals play an important part in Welsh culture and many were used to foretell disaster and death. The most fearsome were the *Cwn Annwn* or the Hounds of Hell which often were seen roaming the Taff and Rhondda valleys as well as the vales of Glamorgan and Neath. The dogs came in all shapes and sizes, some in weird colours too. Their favourite haunting grounds were crossroads where a hanging had been carried out, or any place where a murder had been commited.

Seen singly these dogs were considered to herald the coming of sickness but a whole pack meant death in the family. Those terrible hounds were greatly feared by the people of Glamorgan who were convinced that their bark was a sure sign that some dead person's soul was being dragged through the air and taken to some place of misery.

They often were accompanied by *Mallt y Nos* or Matilda of the Night, a Norman lady who, it is claimed, came to Glamorgan with Robert Fitzhamon. When he eventually subdued the Welsh people, life did not hold the same excitement for him. Bored he returned home to his native Normandy for a while. When he returned to Wales he was accompanied by Matilda, a very beautiful fair haired woman with a heart of steel whose main interest was hunting. Often she could be seen riding her black stallion with the hounds and is reputed to have said that, if there was no hunting in heaven, she would prefer not to go there.

One day she met an untimely death when, whilst chasing a pack of hounds across the downs, her horse reared near a cliff throwing her over the edge to the rocks below. Obviously no hunting was allowed in Heaven because after her death Matilda could be seen wearing a red hooded cape and riding her black stallion furiously over the downs, accompanied by a chorus of howling dogs. Her favourite time to appear was on Christmas night, New Year's Eve and, of course, St David's Day, 1st March.

In another tale one dog was seen near the Wilton crossway in the Vale of Glamorgan. The upper part of the body was semi-human

whilst the lower resembled a light coloured spotted dog. Two fierce moon-like eyes stared from its face and, it is said, its stare could cause a person to faint immediately.

Another large black dog of the Hounds of Hell pack haunted an old manor house whenever there was illness or death. It was a quiet dog, almost lazy in its movements, and wasn't afraid of the household, gardeners or gamekeepers. When a member of the family was taken ill the dog would lay in the hall at the bottom of the stairs and remained there until the patient recovered and then disappeared, never to be seen again.

On another occasion a man was making his way home after a day's fishing. It was a cold winter's night and the wind was whistling through the trees. When he came to a crossroads he saw a large white dog lurking in the shadows which stared at him, baring its teeth and growling menacingly. The terrified man backed away as the dog lunged forward as if to attack him. He turned and fled, but in his haste to get away he slipped and fell. He could only watch in terror as the dog advanced on him, and think of his life which was about to end. The hound stood over him looking for a minute and then, with a mournful howl, grew faint and slowly vanished before his eyes.

Squire Morgan's Will

It is hardly surprising to find that in a lyrical country like Wales many of the old legends and true events have been turned into rhyming ballads. The Welsh earned a comfortable living wandering round the country side singing these narratives to the accompaniment of the harp. The story of Squire Morgan's will is a true story and was the subject of one such folk song.

Morgan was a bachelor who lived with two maiden sisters near Cowbridge nearly two hundred years ago. He was very wealthy and owned many estates which had been handed down through many generations. His sisters sole aim in life was to care for their brother's every whim and fancy. It never occurred to them that he may have been happier if he had been allowed to marry. The elder dominatintg sister knew her brother thought only of today and was concerned that he had made no plans for their old age. The squire had always been a healthy man and the thought of making a will had never entered his head, although his sister did mention it on several occasions.

One September morning Morgan was taken ill suddenly. Although it did not incapacitate him it did set him thinking about making a will because he knew that, if he died inestate, his sisters would lose their home and possessions. Everything would go to the next male heir, another sister's son called Jack Hill, who, although a good natured man, enjoyed spending money. The old squire knew his fortune would soon be spent if Jack inherited.

Morgan called his two sisters and told them he had not made a will and felt it was time he did. They called John the coachman to explain the situation and, according to the ballad, he went for help immediately:

'he saddled at once, and did not spare
The whip and spur on the good black mare.'

John first called on the doctor who unfortunately had already begun his day's rounds and was not expected to return until late afternoon. He left a message for the doctor to call on the squire as soon as possible. John remounted his horse and dashed to lawyer Lewis' home. Although he was at home, he was hard at work on some deeds which had to be put on the London coach later that day and would not be free until the document was finished. John explained how important his mission was and begged the lawyer to come quickly. Lewis expressed his sympathy and hoped the squire was not as ill as they thought but he would come as soon as possible. John was shown into the kitchen and given food and drink while he waited for the lawyer to complete his work. John waited most of the day and then, deciding he could wait no longer, jumped up and made for home. He raced as fast as he could, and reached the stables just as the clock was striking eight.

During the day the old Squire had deteriorated and gradually lapsed into unconsciousness. As the ballad says, his sister Joan, realised what it would mean to her and her sister if he died without making a will:

'If Morgan died without a will,
and all the estate went to young Jack Hill,
What was to come of them, old and grey?

'And Morgan slept.
Whilst o'er the world the twilight crept;
And just as dark shrouded hill and down,
They found that in sleep his soul had flown
Out of the world, and would never come back,
And all his wealth would belong to Jack!'

With Morgan dead, Joan thought for a while and then, in unspoken prayer, muttered:

'Now God forgive me for what I do.'

She called her younger sister Elizabeth, who was horrified at her sister's plans:

'Elizabeth don't whine and cry;
Go, call that John, and send him down
For Jacob Harding of the Down.'

Jacob Harding, an old trusted friend of Morgan, was called for. He was a Quaker shoe-maker, well respected in Cowbridge and very similar in appearance to the squire. They dressed alike and it was often very difficult, even for the sisters, to tell them apart. Jacob arrived and was quickly ushered into the dead man's room. Once the door was closed, Joan quickly disclosed the plan to put the squire's body under the bed with Jacob slipping into Morgan's nightgown. Then he would impersonate the squire and give instructions for the will:

'Jacob listened and shook his head.'

Jacob didn't want to be party to this plan, but Joan tried persuading him with the promise that he could live rent-free in the house where he lived with his family and want for nothing.

'Jacob pondered, wished and sighed.'

After much soul searching he agreed it was a good idea. After all Joan and Elizabeth would get what rightly belonged to them and he, his wife and children would benefit too. Then, his Quaker conscience began to worry him but it was too late because outside they could hear the sound of horse's hoofs on the cobbled courtyard. When the sound stopped there was a sharp knock at the door.

'Please ma'am, the lawyer has arrived,' said the old servant woman.

Turning to the sisters Jacob asked them to help him change. Quickly and quietly they placed the body under the bed and Jacob took his place in the bed.

Presently the lawyer was called into the room, and Jacob pretended to be the squire and gave instructions for the will.

'Morgan's wealth of house and land,
Stock and furniture, and grand
Crested silver, shining line,
All went to the shaking women.'

Suddenly Jacob realised that it was within his power to will himself anything he wished and the sisters were powerless to intervene. His heart began to beat faster, his breathing became more uncertain, and his voice faltered and broke as he thought of the sin he was about to commit. The lawyer, fearing that the squire would die before the will was made, suggested a brandy and, after Jacob was revived, he continued.'The house in which my old friend Jacob Harding lives, and the garden, I leave to him, also the orchard and the field known as the poor man's pretty meadow.' More brandy was administered, and by now Joan was looking at

121

him in disbelief. He cleared his throat and continued, 'The clover field adjoining this meadow I leave to Jacob too.' Jacob had only enough strength left to sign the will, and the lawyer left congratulating himself that he had arrived in the nick of time.

Jacob then rose, dressed and departed quickly, pleased with his performance.

Time passed and the friendship between the old squire's family and Jacob became more distant with bitterness until finally it ceased altogether. Also, during the time since Morgan died, the Quaker had no luck, his life had changed and he had aged considerably. His wife had long since died. His much loved daughter had died tragically in the snow. His sons, Ben and Billy, had left home to adventure in foreign lands. Only his youngest daughter, Kate, remained at home, and even she was not there when his final hours arrived.

As Jacob lay dying a kindly neighbour was called to sit with him, but she felt that Jacob could not allow himself to die. He rambled on in his weakness, and muttered about his old friend the squire, of his death, and of a lawyer's visit and a will. The neighbour listened intently and finally sent for the vicar who, much to Jacob's relief, came at once. His face lit up when the vicar entered his bedroom.

'T'was good of thee to come, old friend,' said Jacob. Then with a clammy hand he grasped the vicar's hand and confessed all:

'I thought to leave my boys this house and land;
It was ill-gotten, and I cannot stand before my Maker.
Take thou those deeds, and put things straight.
See thou restore it all to young Jack Hill,
And tell him how I made Squire Morgan's Will.'

His mission accomplished, Jacob rested his head on the pillow and fell into a deep and everlasting sleep.

The Maid of Sker House and other Legends

Sker House was originally built by abbots from Neath Abbey as Sker Manor to live in when they farmed the surrounding land. It is situated some way from the village of Newton-Nottage overlooking the sea. After the Dissolution of the Monasteries, the de Turberviles — descendants of the Norman Knight of the Conquest of Glamorgan — took up residence. The family remained Catholic after the Restoration. Sker House became a meeting place for the Roman priests who used to hide in the recesses between the thick walls when danger loomed. Today it stands derelict and spooky, surrounded by a wilderness of heath and sand. Once seen it is easy to understand why so many romantic and strange legends have been written about it.

Despite its long history the first legend, written in Welsh with the title '*Y Ferch o'r Seer*' did not appear until the nineteenth century. As with many tales the origins are obscure.

The story goes that Isaac Williams of Sker had two daughters, Elizabeth who is the maid in our story, and Mary. Elizabeth was tall, beautiful and enjoyed dancing. She would eagerly await for the local Mabsant — the festival to commemorate the local saint, Mary Magdalen, which took place in the local Town Hall. A harpist would play throughout the night and everyone, even the old women, would attend. One year the harpist was Thomas Evans of Newton-Nottage who was immediately attracted the Elizabeth. It was love at first sight and they spent most of the night together. By dawn they had become lovers.

When Isaac heard of the relationship he was furious. He was a gentleman farmer and expected better for his daughter than a harpist who was a carpenter by trade. Undeterred Thomas decided to elope with Elizabeth and hired a carriage and pair. Unfortunately on the night of the elopement, as they were about to leave the dogs heard them and made a commotion. Immediately the old house sprung into brightness as candles and lamps were lit. Thomas made a hasty retreat and Elizabeth was left to face her father. Furious he pushed her into her room, locked the door and forbade her to go out. She pined so much for her lover that Isaac decided to force her to marry a Mr Kirkhouse of Neath in the hope that she would forget Thomas. But like most arranged marriages, the pair were ill-matched and spent most of their time quarrelling. Thomas returned frequently to see Elizabeth and once her husband caught them together.

Nine years later she died of a broken heart and was buried in Llansamlet Churchyard on 5 January 1776. Sadly the tombstone has disappeared and lies buried in an unknown part of the churchyard.

Thomas Evans, however, got over his infatuation, married at fifty and had several children. In 1819 he collapsed whilst playing his harp at a ball in Nottage Court and died a few weeks later. He is buried in Newton Churchyard.

Anyone who reads the book 'Maid of Sker' by R.D. Blackmore hoping to find the story of this legend, will be disappointed because his story bears no resemblance to the original legend. Blackmore, who was the son of John Blackmore and Anne Bassett, was born in 1825 and lived at Nottage Court. He wrote *The Maid of Sker* at the court. He spent his childhood in Nottage and grew to love the area as much as he grew to love Devon and Exmoor.

In Blackmore's book the central character is David Llewelyn, a fisherman and sailer of Newton-Nottage. Only a small part of the book is devoted to the heroine. The story opens with David, already old, living in retirement in a cottage facing Newton Green. He manages somehow to rejoin the navy and fight in the French wars for eighteen years. The Maid of Sker was published three years after *Lorna Doone* and was considered inferior, even by Blackmore. Even so it is still worth reading for its vivid descriptions of the countryside around the coast and the two counties the author loved so much.

As might be expected Sker House has its ghost and, according to local people, it is that of the original maid. She has been seen in an upstairs room, possibly the one in which she was imprisoned by her father. In Blackmore's story the maid also had a secret place within the house called the Abbots Walk. For a ghost she is noisy and the sound of heavy clunking chains can be heard.

There is supposed also to be a ghost of a quarrelsome monk who fell out with his Holy brethren, met an untimely end and frightens the occupants by groaning in the middle of the night.

Sker also has a visitor in the shape of a stone. This stone, thought to be the prehistoric relic that lies in a field off Water Street, is said to visit the beach on Christmas morning before the cock crows. It takes a drink from the water's edge and then returns to its normal site. It is said that anyone who is unfortunate to see it and crosses its path will meet a fateful end.

The First Recorded Fairy Tale

We can safely assume that story telling dates back to Neolithic times, but the first fairy-tale to appear in book form was written by Giraldus Cambrenis or Gerald of Wales in about 1190. He gathered his material when he accompanied Archbishop Baldwin on a tour of Wales in 1188 to preach the Crusades. On his return Giraldus wrote an account of his travels, entitled '*Itinerary Through Wales*' which was followed by '*The Description of Wales*'. Today an edited edition of both books is available as a single volume in the Penguin Classic Series and is well worth reading for its vivid descriptions of everyday life in 12th century Wales.

In the original version Giraldus recorded his journey through the Vale of Neath and told of local legends. One was the story of a priest, Elidorus, and the strange incident that happened to him when he was a child.

From an early age Elidorus was destined for the priesthood and was made to read and write. But he was not a willing pupil, preferring to day dream, and was often in trouble. One day when he was twelve he ran away to escape punishment and hid himself under a hollow near the bank of the River Neath. After two days, when he was very hungry, two little people came up to him and promises to take him to a land full of delights and sport. Thrilled at the prospect Elidorus quickly followed them through an underground passage. Soon they emerged into a beautiful country where it was twilight. The men and women were very small, all had long golden hair and lived on a diet of milk and safron. Instead of riding horses they rode greyhounds.

Elidorus was taken before the king and recognised the place as somewhere his people used to dance and play sports. After much questioning the king introduced him to his young son, who was the same age. The two boys had much in common and played games with a golden ball. After a while Elidorus returned home and told his mother of his adventures with the little people. On several occasions he returned to the twilight world and, after each visit, told his mother a little more. He told her about he furniture and the cooking utensil and how everything was made of gold which glistened in the twilight world. One day she asked him to bring her a present of gold. On his next visit, whilst playing with the king's son, he stole the golden ball and ran down the underground tunnel. When he was almost at the end of the passage he stumbled and fell. The two men who had taken him to the magical country seized the ball and threw him out. Elidorus tried on many occasions to find the entrance to that mysterious world, but never succeeded.

Deeply saddened he returned to his studies and eventually became a priest. Throughout the rest of his life he was unable to talk about his childhood without shedding tears for the enchanting world he lost.

The exact location of the entrance to that strange land has never been identified although, from the description of the fair court, it is thought to be Pont Neath Fechan near Craig-y-Ddinas. Here tradition recalls that local people held dances and sports where the river Neath meets the river Mellti.

King Arthur Sleeps On

For our last story we stay in the same area, Craig-y-Ddinas near Pont Nedd Fechan at the top of the Neath Valley. This is a fitting setting for one of the most famous cave tales about King Arthur and his Knights. In common with Glastonbury in England, it claims to be the site of King Arthur's Avalon. There are many places in Wales called Craig-y-Ddinas and all claim to be the resting place of King Arthur and his Knights.

It is said that after fighting his last battle against the Saxons, King Arthur and his twelve Knights, marched towards Craig-y-Ddinas. As they passed through the hamlets and villages the Knights noticed that the king was looking very tired and asked him if he wanted to rest.

'No,' replied their leader who marched on defiantly until, exhausted and hot, they reached a grassy hollow. There, in the coolness of the evening, they laid down to rest.

One by one the men fell into a deep and restful sleep. As it grew dark *Y Ladi Wen* — The White Lady — glided towards the hollow where the men were resting. Meanwhile, an old woman, the Knowing One of the village cried out that Vivien the Witch was in the area. The villagers came out of their cottages to see, but said it was only the white mist of evening and a sure sign that tomorrow would be another hot and sultry day. The old woman was not convinced and decided to see for herself. When she arrived at the grassy hollow at Craig-y-Ddinas she saw the king and his men sleeping and feared Vivien had charmed the men into a deep sleep. She decided to stay with the men until morning and made herself comfortable behind a hazel bush on a mossy bank opposite. Suddenly the moon disappeared from view and she was surprised, that even in the darkness, she could see the paleness of the men's faces. As she continued to look the brightness of their faces began to dazzle her, until eventually it was as though she was looking straight at the moon. Mesmerised by the brightness she soon fell asleep and, when at first light she woke, the king and his men had gone. Where they had rested she saw an opening to a huge cave which was not there the previous evening. She got up and, as she was about the enter, the entrance suddenly closed.

She returned to the village and told everyone that Vivien had lured the king and his men into an enchanted cave, but no one believed her.

Many hundreds of years later a Welsh drover was standing on London Bridge after taking his animals to Barnet Fair. He was tired after many days of travelling and was resting on a long stick cut from a hazel bush during his journey. He was about to leave to find shelter for the night when he noticed a stranger staring at him. The stranger then came over to him and spoke.

'Where did you get that stick?' he enquired.

'What's it to you,' answered the drover, irritated by the question.

'It's nothing to me, but it could be of great importance to you. It could lead you to silver and gold.'

The drover became interested and asked the stranger to explain what he meant.

'Hazel bushes can be used to find treasure. In a dream I saw a place where treasure was hoarded. Tell me where you found that stick, and I will tell you where to find treasure.'

The next day the two men set out for the Neath Valley and the following day the drover took the stranger straight to the grassy hollow where he had cut his stick.

'This is the place that I saw in my dream' said the stranger excitedly. 'Quick fetch a spade and dig where I tell you.'

The drover did as he was told and shortly he came across a large flat stone. Together they moved the stone and found steps leading down into a long passage, in the middle of which was a bell.

'Whatever you do,' said the stranger, 'don't touch the bell.'

The two men proceeded along the passage until they reached a huge cave lit by a single lamp. They entered and found hundreds of soldiers asleep in a large circle wearing armour and with their swords unsheathed ready for action. Inside the circle were twelve Knights plus one other with a golden crown encrusted in jewels upon his head.

'That's King Arthur,' said the stranger proudly. 'The others are his twelve knights and their army of soldiers. They are all asleep waiting for the day when the Black Eagle and the Golden Eagle shall make war upon one another. When it happens the noise will be so loud that it will shake the earth and the bell will ring so loudly that everyone will wake and destroy the enemies of the Welsh. Then King Arthur will re-establish his court at Caerleon, and rule the island of Britain again.'

The stranger showed the drover two large piles of silver and gold alongside the sleeping king and his knights.

'You may enter the charmed circle and take as much as you like from one pile, but you cannot take from two piles at the same time.'

The drover hesitated at first, but the stranger reassured him that the knights were in a magical sleep. He filled his pockets with silver, but the more he took, the pile never seemed to get any smaller. Again, the stranger warned him not to touch the bell but, if he did touch it, he was to remain calm. If this happened one soldier would lift his head and ask if this was the day. The drover was told if he valued his life he should tell the soldier that the day had not dawned and he was to go back to sleep. The stranger and the drover then left the cave and the next morning the stranger set off for London.

Day after day the drover visited the cave bringing back gold and silver on alternate days. One day he was careless and brushed against the bell. Immediately one of the soldiers lifted his head and asked if it was the day. The drover quickly gave the correct response and the soldier lay down his head and went back to sleep.

One day the drover had greedily taken too much gold and was very excited In his struggle to carry more he stumbled and fell against the bell and dropped the gold. The soldier raised his head and asked the question but the drover was too busy retrieving his treasure to answer immediately. Within minutes he was surrounded by soldiers, eyes glaring at him, hands on their swords. He tried to flee but the soldiers grabbed him, dragged him into the centre of the circle and beat him until he almost lost consciousness before taking him to the cave entrance and throwing him out. The soldiers drew back the stone over the passageway and returned to their sleep.

The drover never recovered from his beating and from that day onwards he became a poor man. He and his friends often went to

Craig-y-Ddinas searching for the entrance to the cave but never found it.

As far as I know, the treasure is still there. Perhaps one day you will be lucky enough to find it, but don't forget, if you do, only take from one pile at a time, and DON'T touch the bell.

SELECTED BIBLIOGRAPHY

Marie Trevelyan, *Folklore and Folk Stories of Wales*, London, 1909).
Marie Trevelyan, *Glimpses of Welsh Life and Character*, (London, 1893).
Gwyn Jones, *Welsh Legends and Folk Tales*, (Oxford University Press, 1955).
T. Gwynn Jones, *Welsh Folklore and Folk Customs*, (D.S. Brewer, 1930).
D. Parry-Jones, *Welsh Legends and Fairy Lore*, B.T. Batsford, 1953).
W.T. Barber, *The Visitors Guide to Historic Places of Wales*, Moorland Publishing, 1984).
Gwyn Williams, *The Land Remembers — A View of Wales*, (Faber and Faber, 1977).
Marianne Robertson Spencer, *Annals of South Glamorgan*, (W. Spurrell and Sons 1913).
E.H. Rowland, *A Biographical Dictionary of Eminent Welshmen 1700 — 1900*, (Helen Elwy, 1907).
C.J.O. Evans, *Glamorgan Its History and Topography*, (William Lewis 1938).
P.H. Jeffery, *Ghosts Legends and Lore of Wales*, (Old Orchard Press)
Lewis Thorpe, *Gerald of Wales*, (Penguin Classics, 1978)

The Haunting of Glamorgan and Gwent

RUSSELL GASCOIGNE

Glamorgan and Gwent are the two most highly populated counties in Wales. And they have more than their share of ghostly tales too. From strange sounds to be heard in attics and on the stairs, through doors opening and closing seemingly of their own accord to mysterious apparitions of White Ladies, ghostly carriages and spectral figures glimpsed fleetingly in ancient households before disappearing back into thin air again. The Haunting of Glamorgan and Gwent records numerous examples of such other-wordly phenomena. Here there are tales of shipwrecks, pirates and smugglers, of haunted castles, crumbling ruins and remote farmhouses . . . of rattling chains, screams in the night and terrifying encounters with the world of the paranormal.

Price: £3.75

ISBN: 0-86381-262-7

Gwasg Carreg Gwalch